CW00738785

ISBN 1 872568 35 1

Born Under A Bad Sign

Robert Smith

The Bluecoat Press

Born under a bad sign,
I've been down since I began to crawl,
If it wasn't for bad luck,
I'd have no luck at all.

Albert King, bluesman

Born Under A Bad Sign

Robert Smith

Foster Parents

'Ow! That hurt me, you!'

His elbow had struck me in the face and the fact that he'd begun to laugh meant I had to react. So, like a cat, I pounced, wrestling him to the carpet. We didn't hear the footsteps, but our hearts jumped as the bathroom door crashed open. There she stood, framed in the doorway.

'What the fuck's all this then? Get in yer beds r-r-r-right now!' That stammer spelt big trouble for us. By the time she'd rolled her second r, I was in bed, the blankets quickly drawn over my face. I knew my mate had done the same.

My name is Robert, Robert Suilerman and, at six years old, I was a real handful. My mate's name was Mark Jordan. He was younger than me but we were like brothers, inseparable, or so I thought. I'd known Mark since we were both babies. I remember watching his small brown face staring back from the cot beside mine. There were plenty of cots inside the long room and lots of babies, just like us.

From the time I discovered the world had a blue sky, that grass grew green but trees grew taller, that flowers, insects and animals also lived there, I was with my mate, Markie.

'You think I'm putting up with your behaviour? You're like monkeys! Monkeys! You wait 'till he gets home, we'll see, won't we? Yes, yes we will.'

I wanted to be big, right there and then, so that I could leap from my bed and knock her down. I hated her, so did Mark. We both wished we'd stayed at the Manor with all the other kids. Why did we have to end up with such horrible people? They'd both been so nice at first but that had been a nasty trick, they'd changed so quickly. We hardly saw him unless we were naughty but that meant we saw him enough because, according to the Purdys, we were always naughty.

Thinking back, I can remember the first time we'd met them. It was a cold winter's morning when they arrived at the Manor unexpectedly. Most of us, the kids that is, were outside playing in the mud. The large grounds of Morley

Manor Children's Home swallowed us, as did its huge Edwardian hallways and bedrooms. It must have been '66 because I was born in '61 and I was five years old.

My last birthday party had been held, as usual, inside the great hall. Its floors had been highly-polished and it was full of kids who all lived within the walls of the big Manor.

The five, long, wooden tables rattled as we all tucked into wobbly jelly and drank fizzy pop out of yellow plastic beakers. There were three kids and myself who had to sit on the stage. It was November, nearly Christmas and there had been nine birthdays that week. Fortunately, the other five were still in nappies and we were, therefore, the main centre of attention. That had been a year ago, right now we were both in danger.

'Just make a sound, you know what will happen! Don't yer? Don't yer? Yes – yes yer do!' With her final threat, to our relief the door closed. It wasn't until I heard her footsteps reach the bottom of the stairs that I dared exhale.

'Why did they pick us?' asked Mark from under his blankets.

'Cos they did and … and … just go to sleep now, it's best to, before he gets back.'

'Rob?'

'Yes?'

'D'yer reckon I could fight the boy next door. Do yer? Hey? Do yer?'

'Yes, Markie.'

'Rob!'

'What?'

'Don't let the bed bugs bite.'

'No, I won't, I'm going to sleep now.'

'But, Rob!'

'Shut up now, Markie, okay?'

'Okay!' He knew when I was angry and did what I said. I soon fell asleep and began to dream of home; the Manor, in its full glory, the only home I'd ever known.

Morley Manor, situated in rural Derbyshire, was surrounded by acres of green and brown fields. The wheat and the corn swayed in the breeze that blew across the farmer's fields. His animals frequently visited us, so did Vinny the fox but he always scared off all the rabbits. There was also Jimmy the squirrel, Sid the grass snake, some field mice and plenty of rats. As I slept, I could almost smell the polish on the wooden floors. I rolled over and seemed to wake. There was a sound, at first a faraway sound, a baby crying. It had been crying for such a long time. Where? Where was it coming from? It wasn't him next to me; I knew his cry but there were so many of us here. Who would join in next? Should I? Wait, there's another whimper coming from over there. Good, she'll have to come out now. Yep! here she comes. It's time I rattled my cot bars. 'Hey! Hey! Over here! I'm over here. Me … me … ME!' I wanted some attention. Of course I did, I was lonely, so lonely. I stood up and really began to shake the bars. The whole cot began to rock. 'Me … me … me!' The noise level erupted, all the cots inside the hall began to shake. The sudden commotion of a thousand rattling cot bars frightened me. 'Hey! Hey! Over here! I'm over here, Me … Me … ME … ME!' I covered my ears with my small hands and turned towards the cot in the far corner. She was bending over it and I could hear her talking. She was talking to me. It was my cot. Suddenly, I felt my little feet leaving the mattress, I was floating, floating on thin air, higher and higher, so high I could nearly touch the ceiling. Wow! it was a multi-coloured baby factory. The huge hall was full of cots and all the cots were full……

I could still vividly remember the day when the Purdy's came to the Manor looking for two children to foster.

'Come on now, children!' We were all being hustled in from the yard, the excitement high amongst us. We all knew there would be potential families waiting to see us. Many of them were childless couples looking to build a family. Mark and me were to be fostered together, so we hoped that this time the people were looking for two kids. Most of them would visit the Manor at least once or twice a year. If they found any children they desired, they'd begin to visit more frequently. Usually, it wasn't long after this procedure before the lucky kids vanished. So this time, I closed my eyes and prayed, 'please God, let it be our turn, please God, hear my cry!' They were slowly moving up the line towards us. Mark was smaller than me with a lighter complexion. He stood in front and I began to feel his wavy Afro tickling my nose.

It was a large, fat man who seemed to take some kind of liking to us. His wife looked set on two small girls, further up the line but they had a baby brother; that made three and the Purdys only had room for two, so that was that. Four weeks later, we became the lucky ones, we were leaving the Manor. Yes, for the first time in our short lives, we were to travel along the open roads. We'd both seen so many others drive through the big iron gates, now it was our turn.

I'll never forget that long journey through the Derbyshire countryside and onto Norwich. My mate Mark was sick all over the back seat. He had managed to hold it down until we'd reached our new driveway, when he decided to show the Purdys what we'd had for breakfast.

'I can see scrambled eggs!' I shouted from the back seat. Fat Frank Purdy didn't find this funny but his wife Sheila was in fits of laughter. That was the first and last time we'd ever hear Sheila laugh but, for now, we were all happy, except Frank. At last, we'd found a real family, so Markie and I were extra happy.

'You can call me Mummy and my Frank ... Daddy. Okay kiddies?'

'B-but, what about, er, erm?' I didn't know quite how to say it but she thought she knew exactly what I was trying to say.

'Oh! They're all colour-blind in this street, don't you worry.' Well, that wasn't what I was trying to say. I wanted to know if Markie and me were now real brothers.

'Anyway, who gives a t-toss what the neighbours think,' she added.

Miserable

It was a Saturday. I knew this because the food cupboards were empty. It must have been shopping day. Mark and me had been up since around 6.30. The time had flown and it was now what the Purdys called 'nine-ish' because I could hear Fat Frank stumbling to the bathroom upstairs. We were both sitting in the living room, in front of the television. Frank James Purdy was a sick man with a quick temper. He also possessed a permanently miserable, fat, red face. I think the fact that he'd worked in the same car factory all his life didn't help or that both he and Sheila were on the verge of alcoholism.

Our favourite cartoon had just started; Tom had a broomstick and was chasing Jerry around their cartoon living room. Mark was in stitches on the Persian rug in front of the set but my full attention was focused on the movements of Fat Daddy Frank and I could hear him barging about in the bathroom above us.

'Hey, Sheila! Where's my razor?'

'Oh, no! His razor.' I knew we were in trouble.

'It's in the cabinet, Frank!'

'No, it ain't, Sheila, no, it ain't!'

I wanted us to be the 'Tomorrow People', so that we could disappear as they did on the telly. His dumb razor; Mark had brought it into our bedroom earlier and I'd left it under one of the beds.

Tom had just tripped over the broomstick. Flying through the air, he came to a sudden nasty halt against the cartoon brick wall. A large, pink lump quickly appeared on his head and Jerry walked off with all the cheese but I didn't hear Mark laugh. He wasn't laughing anymore. His eyes were glued to the stairs – so were mine.

'It's fucking them. It's them fucking kids, Sheila.' At the sound of Frank's curse, Mark moved swiftly up from the floor, preferring a seat closer to me. Now he too could feel the storm coming.

'Hey, you lot! Get up here, like NOW!' His bloated, red, face appeared at the top of the stairs. By the time we'd reached the top step, Sheila was out of bed to observe the proceedings.

'Where is it? Hey, where is it?'

Now in these situations, Markie had a tendency to wet his pants. The more Fat Frank's face went red with rage, the closer Markie's bladder would get to losing control; he had already stained one of the rugs downstairs and I knew this would turn the storm into a hurricane. All we needed now was for Sheila to go into one of her frightening fits. We saw them all too often. I knew I had to speak up. Mark now had the tightest grip on my arm and, as Fat Frank's huge face began to bear down on us, his grip got even tighter.

'Where is it? My fucking razor. Where is it?'

'I'll get it!' Moving swiftly, I darted around his legs, closely followed by Markie. Fat Frank was hot on our heels. Purdy was in his element now and was purposely trying to make me panic. I had dropped to my knees and scrambled into our world, under the bed. Retrieving the razor, I spun round and darted back into the real world.

'How the fuck did that get there then? Hey? Hey? You lot started stealin' now, have yer? Hey, have yer?'

I had his silly razor in my outstretched hand, trying to return it to him but that wasn't good enough. Snatching it from me, he nearly wrenched my arm from its socket. He then spun around to focus his attention on little Markie. I knew he would, he always did.

'Hey, you come here!'

Mark was so frightened, he couldn't move. He'd already wet himself, not that it mattered in here, it was only our bedroom. Sheila had appeared at the door and, as usual, was enjoying the whole episode. Frank grabbed hold of Markie by the scruff of his neck and began to shake him. Mark was crying and I was getting angry. He'd got his stupid razor back but he was starting his silly games again. Before I knew it, I was also crying.

We were lucky that day. It was Saturday and Fat Frank had to return to work after our shopping trip. Realising he didn't have time to play, he flung Mark in the direction of the mattress before storming back into the bathroom. I was still crying, so was Mark. Sheila was watching us from the door. She was gloating but I didn't care, we both knew he did the same to her as well, when the mood took him.

Sheila Purdy was a thin, red-haired woman who seemed to thrive on fear. She also had a bad temper of her own and would regularly have what we called 'fits'. Her outbursts would take place at mealtimes when, for reasons known only to her, she would 'flip' and send knives, forks, plates and cups flying in all directions. The first time we experienced one of her tantrums, Markie urinated on her new rug which only made matters worse. That was the first time she hit one of us. I'll never forget the hand-print the slap left on Markie's face, or the fact that I then also urinated on the rug. Sheila had turned into a she-devil, right before our eyes. I was becoming a nervous wreck, Mark had already become one and was getting worse.

But, like a godsend, four weeks later, Sheila Purdy was the one to suffer a nervous breakdown. Although she was rushed to hospital, we knew nothing about it, until the social workers came. After telling us to pack our bags, they informed us we were going on a holiday, 'only for two weeks,' they said. Fat Frank was pretending to be nice again and insisted on helping us pack upstairs. That's when he gave me the warning: 'Don't you start blabbing yer mouth off and telling any fibs about me, or yer Mummy, okay? Just remember, yer only goin' for two weeks, then yer back. Okay, you lot? Okay?'

Yes, I'll remember, I'll remember the things you've been doing to us. Maybe not right now, because I'm only six but one day I'll suss out why I'm having nightmares with you in them.

'No, I won't tell any fibs, Daddy Frank.'

'Good lad and look out for Mark an' all.'

'Yes, I will.'

With our suitcases packed, we were on the move again, this time on holiday, our destination, the city of Liverpool. It was an even longer journey than the one to Norwich and it was made in silence. The two social workers talked amongst themselves but Mark and me just sat and watched the world passing by at thirty miles an hour. It must have been after midnight when we arrived. I don't remember much about it, except being placed into a nice, freshly-made bed.

New Home

'No, not like that, you stupid thing!'

'Sorry!'

'Put your hands up ... up. That's it, hold them there. Robbie, you come here and watch how I punish this bad breed.'

'Okay, Daddy Frank!'

'You're a good boy. As for him, get yer hands up!'

'B-but what did he do wrong, dad? What did he do?'

'He's not a full shillin', look at him. Look! Now you come here!'

'No, I – I don't want to play that game!'

'You do what I say or join him over there!' Markie, I know he likes hurting him. I wish he'd stop it.

'I said come here, you!'

'Okay, daddy.'

'Good boy, good boy.'

'Hello Robbie, it's time to wake up now!'

'Whe-where am I? Who was that? Where's Markie?'

'Come on now. All the others are eating breakfast, you're our late sleeper. By the way, my name's Julie, Aunty Julie.'

'Where's Markie?'

'Oh! He was up ages ago. Come on, get up, I'll fill the sink for you.'

I'd nearly forgotten our late journey but, observing my new environment, the excitement soon caught up with me. Yes! I realised we weren't at the Purdy's, we were on holiday. Yes! But how long did they say, two weeks? Yep, I guess that's a long time. Great! No more Fat Frank. Great! Great!

I was soon taken downstairs, along a hallway, covered with thick, blue, wall-to-wall carpet. The staircase was huge and the carpet went all the way to the dining room door. Once through the door, I saw a large, round table. All the heads turned to look at me as I was ushered in by Aunty Julie. Markie had already made himself at home and was about to fill his face with a large portion of scrambled eggs. I was taken over to sit beside him. Before I was introduced to the other kids around the table, I was given a large bowl of corn flakes. I sure was hungry that day. I was too busy eating to pay much attention as the other kids' names were called out to me. The food became my first priority and I reached for a plate of scrambled eggs. By the time I'd eaten my fill, most of the other kids had left the table, I could hear them outside in the garden. Markie had finished but he was waiting for me.

'I like this house.'

'Why?'

'Why, don't yer like it?'

'Course I do.'

'Better than the Manor?'

'Better than Purdy's!'

'Eggs are better too.'

Well, if Mark felt the food was better, then things could be looking up for us. Even so, I was pessimistic, 'cos this was just a holiday and I had a feeling it would come to an end.

521 Aigburth Road

We both had to memorise this address, 521 Aigburth Road, which was our new home. We'd found this out a few days ago and couldn't believe our luck. Sheila Purdy had recovered from her breakdown, but was still receiving psychiatric treatment and Fat Frank had been sacked from the car factory – something to do with the foreman. Although this meant that we didn't have to go back to them, the Purdy family would return to haunt me in my nightmares for years to come.

521 Aigburth Road was a large, Victorian town house situated close to Liverpool Cricket Club. The house had its own front and back garden. We loved it. Beyond the large oak door, was a welcoming, thick, soft, fitted carpet. There was a large television room and dining room as well as our playroom at the end of the hallway. The main television room was for the use of the staff and the kids, so we had to be on our best behaviour in there. The playroom, on the other hand, was our turf where we could really let off steam. We even had a large Ferguson stereo and our own television.

With the addition of Markie and me, there were now five lads and three girls living at 521. Trevor Paul was the eldest, he was eighteen, Jimmy Moore was fifteen and Davy Green was eight, a year older than me. Zelda Brown and Sally Getts were both seventeen. Katy Christoppolus, a shy Greek girl, was seven like me. Sally Getts was very unattractive and had plans to join the RAF. Zelda, a large, West Indian girl, was content playing mother to us new kids and Markie was in his element. So was I, when she wasn't placing her hands on my willy.

It wasn't long after our arrival that Trevor Paul, the settler of all telly disputes and petty arguments, left us. Although he was my first role model, he left on unsavoury terms but we hadn't been at 521 long enough to be involved in the internal politics. Jimmy, who was the first real scouser I'd ever met, also left, to live with his parents in a place called Cantril Farm. Meanwhile, Mark and me began to fit in nicely. We started school, attending Gilmour Primary, in nearby Garston. Davy Green and Katy already attended the same school. Davy was in a higher class than me and Markie was in a lower one. I was left with Katy, the shy Greek girl and a class full of hostile looks.

'Come on, Robert! Time for school!' That was Aunty Gwen, she was Welsh, and was our favourite aunty. I was beginning to hate school before I even got there. The uniform consisted of a grey, v-neck sweater, white shirt and grey, short pants. To make things worse, we were made to wear grey ankle-socks. I hated not being able to pull my socks up, so did Markie. Davy was allowed to wear long ones, I couldn't wait until I was eight.

Our first day at school was tense. I was the new boy and even, though I was prepared for a rough ride, I was shocked by the looks I received. Nobody called me names that day but I immediately noticed the nudges and sniggers as I entered the classroom. I began to wonder if I was on the right planet. What were they laughing at? Were they laughing at me? Why? I felt awkward, the grey short pants and socks didn't help. I wanted to go home. I wanted to be beamed aboard 521 right now – over and out.

We knew we weren't white like the other kids but we both wished that we were. I think the problem began when we left the Manor. It was because of them, the Purdys; that was the first time in our sheltered lives that we'd been subjected to verbal attacks about our behaviour and the colour of our skin. Frank Purdy often told Markie he was a 'mixed up' breed and that I was the 'real thing'. I didn't have a clue what he was talking about at the time. It was thanks to our first foster parents that I still had nightmares concerning things I haven't talked about yet.

We both had to go to church and Sunday school each week. As I sat and listened to the vicar giving his weekly lesson, I would be transfixed by the huge cross of Jesus, hanging on the wall behind him. Jesus was white, that meant white was right, white was good, I wanted to be white.

'Our Lord Jesus Christ, cast Satan into the black pit!' shouted the vicar. 'The Prince of Light had defeated the Prince of Darkness!' Darkness, light, black, white, am I good or bad? I was confused, and prayed that Markie wouldn't start asking questions, the way he did. He made me feel awkward, I didn't know the answers to everything. Why were we black? I didn't know.

One wet, miserable, Sunday evening after church, as we prepared our uniforms for school, Markie started. I knew what was coming but this time, Markie had an idea,

'Rob!'

'Yeah?'

'I'm gonna straighten my hair, it can go straight you know!'

'Straight? Like the white boys in school?'

'Yep!'

My hair was tighter-knit than Markie's and he was able to make his hair look really straight. I envied him, even if it only stayed straight until the Brylcreme dried up. Markie would often ask me if I ever wished we were white. The answer needed no debate, it would have made life much easier. I was seven, he was six and the problem often kept us awake at night.

Back at school, a rather large girl, Mary Marble, had tried to befriend me and I was immediately on my guard. Mary was the frequent target of classroom jokers who would taunt her about her weight, which always reduced her to tears. I think the reason why she latched on to me was in the hope that they'd miss the wood for the new tree, and it worked, I became their new source of amusement. That was until my first fight, if you could call it a fight. I was born big and always towered over my peers. Jeffrey Dustin, a wiry little blonde boy, got the wrong idea when he decided it was time to test me out. I knew it had to come, it had already been a full week since my arrival. Home time and I was waiting as usual for Markie outside the primary school entrance, when Dustin approached.

'Hey, you, nigger!'

He was with three of his mates. Fat Mary Marble, who was waiting for her baby brother, was standing beside me. Although she had a weight advantage, she was just a girl, so the scales were balanced in his favour. A dry lump stuck in my throat. I caught sight of Markie coming from the main exit, just as Dustin stepped closer.

'Hey nigger, get back to the jungle!'

By now, Markie was standing beside me but the odds were still in Dustin's favour. Markie had definitely heard what Dustin had said, so now I knew I'd have to react, or explain why I hadn't to Markie later. Moving swiftly around fat Mary, which was a task in itself, I confronted him. His mates began to back off as we squared up. Placing my hands on his chest, I pushed with all my strength, sending him crashing to the tarmac but Dustin quickly recovered, jumping to his feet.

'Get him, Dusty!' shouted one of his mates called Graham. I was later to become good friends with Graham Jones. Dustin swung round to defend himself. I could see his heart was no longer in it. Graham stepped forward and stood beside him;

'Come on then, nig nog!'

Two against one but I wasn't going to back down. That's when Davy Green appeared. Dave, who was half-Indian, half-Welsh, was older than all of us by a year. He pushed himself between Dustin and Graham and moved to stand by me. I was glad to see our new room mate, so was Mark. We knew Davy loved a good fight but his arrival settled the dispute for now. Dustin and his crew realised they were up against the second cock of the third year. I was taller than them, Markie was smaller but fat Mary Marble, glaring at them like they were somebody's food, definitely helped change their minds. So, moving in reverse, they decided to put some distance between themselves and us.

'Black niggers!' they shouted, as they ran off towards Garston Old Road.

The confrontation became the talking point all the way home between Davy, Markie and myself and shy Katy, who we'd met by the local tuck shop.

'Why did they call us nig nogs?' asked Markie. 'What does that mean?'

'I don't know,' I replied.

'Cos yer black,' suggested Davy.

'But I'm not black, I'm brown,' said Markie, lifting his hand to show us his skin.

'But you're nearly black, Rob!' Dave said with a smirk.

'Listen, you're just a Paki from the Welsh mountains!'

'No, I'm not, I'm a full-blooded American Indian!'

'A Pakistani you are. Aunty Gwen told me!' Katy and Markie laughed. I knew Davy was getting angry but I couldn't stop now. I had an audience and he deserved it, calling me black. The slanging match didn't end until our return to 521. I was still angry and hurt and I knew I was in for more stick from the white boys at school the next day.

Family

November 27th and it was my eighth birthday. We'd been at Aigburth Road for a whole year. I had settled as well as I could into Gilmour Primary School, although I was always on my guard. Graham Jones, who was now one of my best mates, attended my birthday party, along with Peter Hughes, another friend. Fat Mary Marble also came; she had now befriended Katy and was a permanent fixture at 521. Great, I was now eight and it was nearly Christmas again.

To me, the world was still a small place. My journeys from 521 to school were my only existence. I knew nothing about anything other than playing war games and watching Mr. Spock but I was eight and certain questions were beginning to trouble me. For example, where was I from? It was Markie who had brought the subject up – the way he did. To be honest, I hadn't thought about it much but Markie insisted on finding out how he came to be. He wanted to know if he had a real mum and dad, like the kids in school, like normal kids.

'A mum and dad. Wow! Real ones, our own real ones!'

The seed had been planted and the thought began to excite us as we lay in our beds that night. I know we both dreamt about it. The next morning we rushed downstairs to confront Aunty Julie. She was in charge, even though she was unqualified and only held the position of deputy. At that time, 521 didn't have anyone in overall charge, the last matron had left just before we arrived. The word was out that a new matron had been found and was due to arrive any day. For now though, it was the deputy matron we had to see. Rushing into the main office, with Markie close at my heels, I asked her:

'Have we got real mums and dads?'

'Not like the P-P-Purdys, our own,' insisted Markie. Aunty Julie told us that she couldn't do anything about it herself but she would ask our social workers.

Months went by. Life for us was just beginning. We were safe and happy. So happy in fact, we forgot all about our quest to find our real parents.

Mid-June, 1969, three days before our annual garden fete and she arrived. She was expected, but not on that day, that's for sure. Even Aunty Julie was caught by surprise at the sudden arrival of Dorothy Crystal. She had come to take charge of 521. It all happened on a Thursday. The weather had been hot, not as hot as the year before but it was hot. We were all eating tea inside the dining room, and it was utter chaos. The discipline at 521 had been slacking off for some time.

Big Trevor Paul had long gone, so had Sally Getts. She had joined the RAF and Trevor, I think, went to jail. Zelda, our adopted teenage mother, was now ruler of the roost. I began to argue with her, particularly every Saturday evening, when 'Peyton Place' came on and 'Garrison's Gorillas' had started on the other channel. I loved 'Garrison's Gorillas' and so did Markie but she would always win the ratings contest because all the other kids would side with her. Markie said she got on his nerves too but I think he liked to watch 'Peyton Place' with her and have his willy warmed. Zelda was good at that.

'Pass the salt!'

'Pass the salt, please!'

'I said, just pass the salt!'

'Mark! You say please!' came the shrill voice of Aunty Julie, who sat at the head of the table 'and Zelda, stop doing that, you should know better ... and you, Robert Suilerman,' she added.

Well, if she could throw the mushy peas at me, then I could do it too. Katy was nearly crying, the tea-time commotion was becoming too much for her. Davy Green had the tray of chips on the table and was eating his way through them. Markie had now disappeared under the table. Aunty Gwen was at the back door trying to prevent Mary Marble and some of our mates from crashing the dining room. That's when the door bell rang. We all heard it ring but no one reacted. It wasn't until the third ring that Julie decided to chance it and leave us unattended. That was a mistake. The pea fight started in earnest.

It was a while before Julie returned. The screaming came from Katy. Davy had pushed several mushy peas down the back of her neck. Zelda had me on the floor, rubbing peas into my hair. Markie was throwing them everywhere and laughing his head off. That's when they came in – led by a man called T. J. Fuller who, I was to learn, was the area manager. He was closely followed by a shattered Aunty Julie and behind her, the new matron of 521. We were all in the dog house that evening. After cleaning up the mess we'd made, we were sent to bed.

The stern look on our new matron's face sent a chill through me. Markie said she looked like a witch but I couldn't help thinking that she might be nice, 'cos she was old.' We'd already experienced living under a tyrannical regime and I just prayed she was okay. The next morning we all queued outside the main office to be formally introduced. Me and Mark went in together. I caught sight of our files as she peered over her wiry, round spectacles at us.

'So, you must be Robert Suilerman and Mark Jordan … hello, my name is Aunty Dot, that's short for Dorothy, and I'm in charge here.'

'Can you find my mum?' came the surprise request from Markie. I'd forgotten all about our quest but my mate hadn't.

'Ah! Yes, well, just leave that one with me for a while … There's a lot to be done. How are things at school?'

'Wow! what a diversion,' I thought, as Markie went on to talk about his new form teacher.

After our little meeting, I came out feeling warm and safe. I liked her almost immediately. She could drive as well and had promised she'd buy a minibus for 521.

'I think they'll get rid of Aunty Gwen,' said Zelda.

'Na! Julie – she's evil,' suggested Davy.

'The cook! The cook!' added Markie.

'Yeah, the cook,' I agreed.

We had all gathered inside the playroom after school that day. This was an unofficial kids' meeting and the rumours had begun. Because the place had been run down, and discipline was at an all time low, we believed someone had to go.

'Who do you think, Katy?' asked Markie.

'She don't know nothing!' snapped Davy. I'd begun to

notice the way Davy was always putting Katy down.

'Neither do you, elephant boy!' intervened Zelda.

That was it, the daggers were out. Big Zelda was giving Davy her drop dead stare. To me, her one-eyed glare was hilarious and I couldn't hold in my urge to laugh. I had a catchy laugh, so it wasn't long before everyone was laughing, including Katy. We were now like a real family – just the five of us. But all of that was soon to change with the arrival of the McPherson siblings and Danny Hawksley.

The McPherson Clan

Nobody received the sack as we had anticipated. Aunty Julie stayed as deputy to Dotty Crystal. Gwen, who was still our favourite, had learnt how to drive and it was one of her tasks to take us to Delamere Forest every Saturday afternoon. Delamere Forest was our stomping ground. As soon as we arrived, we were off. Cowboys and Indians was the name of the game. We ran like mad dogs along the stony paths and amongst the tall pine trees. On one occasion, I couldn't go because I was ill with bronchitis. I was so ill I'd been moved into the sick room. This was quarantine and I'd been in there all week.

That's when they arrived; the McPhersons. There were four of them; three boys and a girl. Her name was Susan; she was the eldest and was eight years old, the same age as me and Katy. She had long brown hair, blue eyes and loved herself. Her brother, John, was seven. He had fair hair, blue eyes and also loved himself. The remaining two brothers were David, who was four, and Patrick, who was only three. That was the McPherson family and they had descended upon us.

It was into my ninth day in bed, which meant I was going to be the last one to meet the new kids. I'd heard that the girl had moved into Katy's room, which was beside Zelda's at the far end of the house. David and Patrick shared a room opposite the sick room. They were both close to the matron's bedroom in order that she could attend to us at night if needed. John McPherson had moved into our room, which meant one of the two spare beds was now occupied.

'The new boy, what's he like?'

'He's okay, seems a bit girlish though.'

'Is he getting on with you and Davy?'

'Yeah, he's getting on with Davy okay but he likes wrestling too much!'

'Who, the new boy?'

'Na, Davy.' Markie had been allowed to visit me. I was getting better and he was keeping me updated with news of what had been going on and what the new kids were like.

'The new girl isn't getting on with Katy!'

'Why's that then?'

'I dunno.'

'Well, find out then!'

'I won't!'

'You will, knob head!'

'Smelly arse!'

'Doggy breath!'

'Erm, erm, dodo head!'

'Turnip face!' The sudden fit of coughing prevented me from continuing our weekly banter. By the time I'd recovered, Markie had left.

It wasn't until the following Monday afternoon that the doctor passed me fit to leave the sick room. All the other kids were at school except the McPhersons who had been out shopping for school uniforms. The two eldest, Susan and John, were due to start at Gilmour Primary the following day.

It was John Mac who I met first. After collecting clean linen from the washing cupboard, I returned to the main bedroom. He was already there, trying his new clothes on. He sat down on the bed as I walked in. I just ignored him as I put my blankets on my bedside cabinet. I knew he was watching me.

'Hi!' came the high-pitched voice.

'Hmm.' I grunted from the back of my sore throat.

'What's your name then?'

'Why?'

'My name's John, John McPherson!'

'Oh!' With my back turned to him, I continued making my bed but this new boy was determined to make me talk to him.

'I've got two brothers and a sister, you know.'

'Have ya?'

'They've come to live here, as well.'

'Have they?'

'Yeah!' Eventually, I turned to check out who I was talking to.

'Yes,' I thought 'Markie was right, he's definitely like a girl.' As he sat there talking, I watched him flick his blonde locks of hair from his eyes, just like the girls at school did.

I soon found an excuse to go downstairs but, to my horror, he followed me. He insisted on introducing me to his younger brothers, David and Patrick. His sister was still out shopping with Aunty Gwen. I couldn't wait until half past four and the return of Mark and Davy from school.

The new kids were 'the new kids' and they weren't 'in'. Not until they'd been there long enough. They were white as well. Not that it had been a problem before, but they all had straight hair, blue eyes and white skin, just like the picture of Jesus hanging in church. As they were new kids, they were getting pampered. I knew it wouldn't be long before resentment and jealousy surfaced.

That evening, we all went upstairs together. It was unusual for Davy, he normally stayed up a bit later. Aunty Dotty, as we now called her, came to say good night and turned off the lights.

'Hey, new boy!'

'Yeah?'

'Can you play football?' whispered Markie.

'No, I hate football, it's too rough!'

'What sport do yer like then?' I asked.

'Erm, erm, rugby. I like rugby!'

'Ha, rugby's worse than football, you fool.'

'Na, I meant cricket. I like cr-cricket!' We all laughed at him. I was feeling in a cruel mood and wasn't about to stop yet. Davy got out of bed and went over to sit at the foot of the new boy's bed.

'Can you fight then?' asked Davy inevitably. He loved fighting.

'No. I can't fight.'

'I'll teach yer then!' he insisted, gripping hold of the new boy's arm.

'Na, Davy, don't, I'm going to sleep now!' I knew I had to intervene. Davy was about to start flinging the new boy around the bedroom. He didn't deserve that. Not yet, anyway.

'Davy! Stop it now!' I could see the gleam in his eyes, as his arm went around John Mac's white neck. Davy had a real problem I reckoned. He always got carried away and I could see the new boy was beginning to fret.

'Here's Dotty!' shouted Markie.

With the threat of Aunty Dot Crystal catching him, Davy released the new boy and scampered into his bed. She wasn't really coming, it was just Markie's ploy to save our new room mate from Davy's half-Nelson stranglehold. I watched the blonde boy. He looked mighty relieved that Davy hadn't been allowed to continue. I felt this was an ace for me to play. I could now use Davy to keep the white boy in check. Davy was a good lad but he wasn't that smart, or so I thought. Anyway, I was about to attempt my first manipulation of one of my elder peers; the strange Davy Green.

Full House

Six months had passed since the arrival of the McPhersons and our new minibus. I hated both of them; the minibus, because it advertised the Barnado's slogan, which was printed across both wings, everywhere we went; and the McPhersons who had become the centre of attention at 521. I hated them just as much as the ugly blue van. All this dislike came to a head one day on my return from school.

'Na, it's my turn, so you lot can scram!'

'No, we was here first!'

'But yer always play that rubbish, don't yer?'

Things were brewing into a full scale argument as I entered the room. Markie was holding a handful of records but it looked like the two McPhersons had beaten him to the record player. They only had one record between them, 'Tie a Yellow Ribbon'. I knew John and his sister had been driving Markie mad playing that stupid tune. We hated the record, so that gave them even more reason to play the damn thing continually. I was just about to team up with my best mate when Dotty Crystal intervened:

'Come on now, stop this!' Her eyes focused on Markie and me, I knew what was coming next.

'You two, you can go out and play, there's still plenty of daylight!'

'But I don't want to,' replied Markie, and I began to frown.

'Well, that's tough luck, off you go!' she replied curtly.

Markie's eyes began to narrow with frustration. I knew how he felt because of the way things had been going lately. We both stormed out of the playroom and I could hear Markie cursing as he brought up the rear. Helping ourselves to apples on the way through the kitchen, we headed for our den in the back garden. We'd built it ages ago with the help of Trevor, before he left. Davy was at a Scout meeting that evening, or he'd have been with us, in the dog house as usual.

'I hate them bloody McPhersons. See, I told yer they always get their own way and don't say it's not 'cos them's white!'

'Alright Markie, alright, stop going on and on at me.'

'It's not you, it's them!'

'Well, them then. Anyway, wait 'till tonight, wait 'till Davy gets back, that girlie boy forgets he shares the same room as us.'

'Yeah, he'd be better off in the girls' room though, wouldn't he, Rob?'

'Yes, Markie, just you wait until Davy gets home. We'll see, won't we? Won't we? Yes, yes we will!' My impersonation of our wicked foster mother, Sheila Purdy, sent Markie into fits of laughter. I laughed as well but I was serious about getting revenge on John 'Girlie Boy' McPherson.

It didn't take long sitting on the floor of the dingy wooden hut before I'd figured out what it was I had to do. I knew I'd have to involve Davy Green. My only problem was in devising a way to do it. If I was to set Davy on Girlie Boy directly, I would be in trouble. John Mac would grass on me straightaway. If it came to the attention of Dotty Crystal, then Davy himself might grass me up. I couldn't allow that to happen. I had to cause them to clash in our room at night. I knew this wouldn't be too hard to accomplish.

'Markie, don't you worry about Girlie Boy, wait 'till tonight.'

By seven o'clock that same evening, we were all ready for bed. Big Zelda wasn't home yet, but we were all having supper in the kitchen. It was Friday tomorrow and our last day at school before the Christmas holidays. We were all excited. Graham and Patrick Mac, the young brothers of John and Susan, had already gone to bed. Anyway, they weren't in the power struggle, although they were sometimes used as pawns. They were too young to understand. Davy Green had returned early from the Cub Scouts. In fact, he'd been sent home for clouting another boy, the second consecutive week that Davy had been sent home for fighting.

'He called me a 'blacky'!' explained Davy, 'so I thumped him in the face.' Davy wasn't playing with a full deck of cards at the best of times but he could certainly handle himself.

Our favourite, Aunty Gwen was overseeing the supper. Aunty Julie had gone off duty and Dotty was in her office. The sound of the front doorbell sent Gwen rushing off to let someone in.

'Yeah, this time I'll do that,' shouted Markie.

'Na, watch me first!' demanded Davy.

The game involved a competition to see who could gargle his luke-warm drinking chocolate the longest. Markie had nearly vomited the previous week, but Davy had reached the count of fifty with his attempt. Shy Katy sat opposite me. She seemed amused by the proceedings. That's when I noticed Susan and John McPherson had stopped chatting away to themselves, the way they did. They were now looking over at us in disgust from the end of the long wooden table. It wasn't long before Davy and Markie directed their attention towards them but, before they had time to spit their chocolate at them, they were stopped by the bedtime call. We all said good night to Aunty Dotty on our way upstairs. The two girls, shy Katy and Susan Mac, now hated each other. They had to make their way to the end of the house to reach their bedroom. We all piled into our room. As usual, Girlie Boy was last one into bed.

'Good night, boys!' shouted Gwen, as she switched off the lights.

'Good night!' came the joint replies. I waited until I heard her footsteps return from the girls' room and hit the bottom step before I sat up.

'Hey, Davy!'

'Yeah?'

'So, a white boy called you 'blacky' today then?'

'Yeah!'

'Did yer give him a good punch then?'

'Yeah, I did!'

'Show us what happened then, Davy.' I knew this request meant he'd have to get out of bed to demonstrate as he always did. Girlie Boy and Markie looked on in amusement. Markie more so – he had a good idea of what was coming next. Davy quickly demonstrated how he had flung his victim to the ground, a detail which he'd obviously added to make the story more dramatic.

'Didn't he try and fight back then?' I asked. The question made Davy swing round to face me.

'What, fight me? No white boy can fight me!' he boasted, pushing out his chest.

'What about me then?' I suggested. Davy looked at me with a sick grin. In fact, all of Davy's grins were sick. He shook his head.

'Na, not you Robbie, you're me mate!'

Glancing at Markie, I knew I'd have to be careful with my

next move. My intended victim was the only white person in the room. I could sense he was already feeling out of place. We knew that feeling very well; feeling out of place. Time was running out on me. I had to make my move now or wait until another night. Looking away from Markie, towards the bed in the far corner, I nodded in a friendly gesture at the bed's occupant, John Mac. I knew Davy was still watching me.

'You alright there?' I enquired in my caring voice.

'Yes, but I'm tired,' came the girlie reply. That was all Davy needed to hear. The sound of Girlie Boy's voice set him off.

'You, you're always tired. Come here, I'll wake yer up,' he ranted, quickly striding towards the white boy's bed. 'Come on, let's fight. Come on!'

'No, no, I don't want to!' Before his sentence was complete, Davy was on him. Grabbing him by the arm, he dragged the helpless John Mac from his bed. Throwing him to the carpet, face down, Davy placed him into a painful-looking arm lock.

'I submit! I submit!'

I giggled to myself, knowing Davy would ignore his plea for mercy. He always did when he was allowed to get carried away. Markie and me would have to intervene but we weren't going to. Not tonight. Markie winked at me from his bed across the room. Davy was now manoeuvring a struggling John Mac into another position; his favourite position, the Boston stranglehold. I laughed as we watched Girlie Boy's white arms and skinny, shapeless, legs struggling to get free. Davy had secured him into a headlock. Girlie Boy's fight to free himself became a fight for air. Davy was squeezing his arm around his neck.

Suddenly, I was captivated. Davy was swinging his head from side to side, as his grip tightened. It was fascinating how quickly his face had turned from white to crimson red. His eyes were squeezed tight but they were beginning to bulge as they opened. It was starting to get a bit noisy now. Girlie Boy's arms and legs were kicking wildly and some blood began to appear from his nose. I should have intervened by now but I didn't. For some reason, I think I was enjoying myself. For some reason, I wanted to see a white person being hurt. I knew the pain. I'd seen Markie suffer pain. Now it was his turn.

Markie coughed. It was designed to attract my attention. I quickly glanced at him. He was looking rather worried now. Girlie Boy was still resisting, although by now his arms and legs seemed to be moving in slow motion. His face didn't look too healthy either. It had gone greyish. Suddenly the white, shapeless, legs stopped kicking and his arms flopped down like a stringless puppet. His face had already turned grey, but he was still moving, in small twitching movements. All I could hear now was Davy's heavy breathing. His eyes were glazed. I knew he was enjoying himself.

'Stop it, Davy, stop him, Robbie, stop him!' That was Markie.

But I was transfixed by it all. I don't think Davy heard Markie's plea either. So it must have been instinct that told him to release his hold on Girlie Boy's neck. The sudden rush of air that entered his lungs sent him into fits of coughing as he gasped for breath. Davy jumped to his feet and banged his chest in triumph before darting back to bed.

Markie had turned his face to the wall. Hear no evil, see no evil. I watched as the white boy dragged himself into bed. I was relieved he wasn't dead or seriously hurt but, for some reason, I wanted to see it all over again. Well, there's always tomorrow night, I thought, as I turned over and went to sleep. I could hear him sobbing and I was glad.

The next morning, Girlie Boy looked in a bad way. We were lucky Aunty Julie, who woke us in the morning, hadn't decided to open the curtains, the way she normally did. She would have seen John McPherson's ghostly appearance and bloodshot eyes. Markie wouldn't talk to me all morning.

It wasn't long before the girls knew something had taken place that evening. What surprised me the most was that we managed to keep it between us. I think the fact that John didn't tell his sister Susan about what had happened earned him our respect. Markie was going out of his way to befriend him now. He had even invited him into the den. I thought that was going too far but I wasn't about to fall out with Markie over John McPherson. Davy told me he hated Girlie Boy. I was later to discover that that was a lie. There was another reason why Johnny Mac didn't grass on Davy for setting on him that night.

The New Kid

His name was Danny Hawksley and, on the Monday he arrived, it was snowing heavily. I had graduated from junior school and now attended New Heys Comprehensive in Allerton, a middle-class Tory area of Liverpool.

Davy, who, I'd hoped, would have paved the way for me by attending last year, had been shipped off to a boarding school in Wales. He had become too much to handle for the teachers at Gilmour Primary. Always fighting, always on guard, he hated being called 'wog' or 'Paki' and always reacted quickly when he was – sometimes too quickly for his own good. I knew how he felt and wasn't looking forward to my first day, the new school was massive. I wasn't starting completely on my own. There was shy Katy but I might as well have been on my own. Katy was Greek and could pass as being white and alright. I was British born, but couldn't pass anyone without feeling they were sniggering or making sly comments.

I remember being told that if anyone called me names, I should tell a teacher. I'd tried that once and was labelled a 'snitcher' as well as all the other hurtful names, so I wasn't about to do it again. Anyway, the way I saw things, I'd perhaps have to be a bit more like Davy. I'd have to fight them, to stop them. Those I couldn't fight I'd avoid. There was a whole heap of fighting to be done. But why? I'd try to figure out why they had to keep calling me those horrible names. Even passing cars would slow down in the street if they saw me, to allow the passengers to shout 'nigger' or 'coon' in my face.

I was eleven, nearly twelve years old, angry and on my own. So angry that I'd been born with brown skin. People seemed to want to hurt me, even the adults that were sent to care for me. I looked at my own reflection in the playroom window.

'Who am I? Where have I come from? Whose son am I?' Old questions returning in my hours of distress but this time I began to feel pains in my head. Throbbing pains. My face was tense. The teeth in my mouth clenched tightly together, creating a grating sound inside my head. I felt like exploding any second.

It had been a miserable day. I was in the playroom feeling sorry for myself, when the doorbell rang. I knew that everyone was at home, therefore it had to be a visitor. Rushing to the window, I saw the scruffiest-looking white boy I'd ever seen standing on the front step.

It was Danny Hawksley and he'd come to stay. He was from Halewood and spoke with the thickest Scouse accent I'd ever heard. He was also the same age as me. After he'd been introduced to everyone, I was given the task of showing him around the house, closely followed by Markie. I began with the back garden and finished in the new staff living room.

'This is for them!' I informed him, watching his eyes quickly scanning the furniture and hi-fi equipment, just as he'd done in the main office. 'D'yer like it?' He didn't answer me. In fact he hadn't said much at all but that all changed at supper time. I sat and listened to him talking like the white boys in school. We were all ready for him to say the nigger word, although he never actually did.

Danny Hawksley was the original scally, he would later teach us all a couple of tricks. It was thanks to Danny that I began smoking and also picked up my first caution for theft. But, at this stage, he was an outsider and, to fit in, he knew he'd have to prove himself. It was during one of his attempts to do this that we clashed, resulting in a fight in the back garden. That was another lesson he'd teach me, that a smaller boy can beat up a taller boy. He left me punch drunk and angry. I was so confident I'd beat the upstart to the ground but he'd ducked and dived, weaved and struck. No matter how hard I tried, I couldn't grab hold of him. I was to find out afterwards that Danny had been boxing since he was five years old. The balance of power was about to shift at 521.

It began, inevitably, with the McPhersons. Davy was at boarding school, so Girlie Boy, who was becoming a pain, had taken to trying to copy the new boy, Danny Hawksley. He was really getting on my nerves. The fact that Danny had given me a good pasting didn't help. Everyone liked him and, even though he was a bad influence on us, the staff liked him too. As the weeks turned to months, the atmosphere in our bedroom was becoming tense. Danny had been allowed too much control. The other lads looked up to him too much, including Markie.

I was to learn another lesson. I observed Danny's quick acceptance into our household and the way we'd all paid homage to him. We'd forgotten the golden rule; always keep newcomers at bay for a while. Although Danny didn't have fits like Frank and Sheila Purdy, he began to show the signs of a bully with his bad temper. I began to feel uncomfortable with him as he began to dictate our movements and thoughts. Danny and me soon fell out again. This time I wasn't going to stand and trade punches. He was too fast, I could never connect him with a solid punch. No, that wouldn't do, I had to catch him off guard.

A full week had passed before I made my decision to do something to Danny. We were on school holiday for a week and Davy was home for the weekend from boarding school. We'd all gone to bed early, with the exception of Danny who had asked to stay up and watch some programme. Davy, Markie and John Girlie Boy McPherson were chatting away together from their beds. I lay with my back to them, listening to their discussion of what had happened that day.

'Danny hit me today 'cos I turned his record off!' complained Girlie Boy.

'Well, you shouldn't have then,' replied Davy.

'But he left it on and went in the garden.'

'So now yer know what he's like, don't yer?' added Davy

'Yeah, we do, don't we!' whispered Markie.

'Don't we just!' I thought to myself but I was determined I

wasn't going to get involved in their debate. For one, we were all to blame for allowing Danny to become a monster. We'd let him walk all over us and I was angry. It was as if he'd tricked us with his wit and daring personality. We had all lived sheltered lives and now this streetwise kid was running rings around us. With his rough upbringing and mentality, Danny Hawksley had not only taught us things for free, he now wanted something in return. He wanted the right to speak to us and treat us how he pleased. I had to do something quickly. He was becoming unbearable.

I could hear him coming up the stairs. Markie and the others had stopped talking about him. I gritted my teeth. I was vexed this was happening. The others had tried to sound out my feelings on the situation but I wasn't getting involved in their talk. I had my own solution to Danny Hawksley. It came in the form of a brown, thick, silver-buckled leather belt that I had under my pillow.

Boom! In through the door he came. My back was turned, but I knew his routine: slippers off, pull back the sheets and climb in. I casually turned round and was watching him as he pulled the sheets over his shoulders. The room was silent. He must have known something was wrong. But the vibes had been like this for some time. With my eyes half open, I watched, waiting for him to turn his back to the wall. It seemed like ages. For a minute, I thought he was staring right back at me but he began to yawn, which was a positive signal for me to move into position. Watching him as he turned to face the wall was a relief. Silently, my feet touched the carpet. I sat up swiftly, the belt gripped tightly in my hand. I began to bite my bottom lip as I rose to a standing position. My heart was beating fast, almost out loud. It was the only sound I could hear as I moved towards him, holding my breath. I was standing virtually above him. The sweat began to run down from my arm pits.

The only sound he heard was the jingle of the silver buckle. That's when his head turned but it was too late for me to stop now. The first blow landed, catching him fully in the face. I quickly repeated the procedure, going into a frenzy.

I didn't hear him scream but I knew he was, as he rolled himself into a ball on the bed to protect himself. I began to whip him about his body. It was lucky for him that he was wearing pyjamas. Very lucky, because I wasn't stopping yet. The thought of him recovering and fighting back spurred me on.

Danny reached the floor and had begun to crawl towards the door. I wasn't stopping him from getting away, but I wasn't about to stop bringing the heavy leather belt down on him either. As we reached the door, I heard footsteps making their way urgently up the stairs. I could hear a voice calling to me, talking to me.

'Rob, Rob, please, stop now Rob!' It was Markie, standing beside me. I had blanked out. I could see Danny on the floor between my legs. He was writhing with pain. I could now hear his screams. Red welts had begun to appear on his pale white skin. I dropped the belt as the first adult appeared at the bedroom door.

'What's going on here?' Danny was still screaming and had dragged himself into the hallway. I calmly walked back to my bed.

'He deserved that,' I thought to myself.

End of a Friendship

'Be bop a loo ya, she's my baby!' I was jumping around the playroom to the music. I'd been left on my own in the house with Dotty Crystal and Mary the cook. All the other kids had gone to Delamere Forest with Aunty Gwen and Aunty Julie accompanying them. I was now a big thirteen year old. It had been over eight months since the whipping incident but I was still on punishments for that and because of my general attitude. Being prevented from going to the forest, or anywhere in the mini, was part of my penance. I was angry, but not about missing the forest trip. I'd begun to hate Delamere Forest.

In fact, I'd begun to dislike almost everything and everybody. I had the music on full blast. It was a wonder that Dotty hadn't come in and turned it down. I'd started to always play loud music whenever I got frustrated and pissed off. Having no-one to talk to any more made matters worse. Davy Green was still at boarding school. John McPherson and his sister Susan hadn't changed, they still got on my nerves. Danny was in love with big Zelda and the feeling was mutual. The young McPhersons, Patrick and Graham were older now but they tended to behave like spoilt brats and shy Katy had become even more introverted and hardly communicated with anyone.

I hated them all, particularly Dotty Crystal, the people who ran the home and all the staff. They'd all allowed it to happen. They had made it happen. Now I was really on my own. They didn't care, or try to understand. He'd been my very best friend in the whole world. He was my brother and now he had gone. The empty bed in our room made it harder for me. Every night since he'd gone, I'd cursed. Every morning, I felt empty. It was like a piece of me was missing. I'd curse him. I'd curse everyone and squeeze my eyes shut real tight and scream the same question inside; why weren't you my real brother. Why? Why?

Yes, Markie had gone. It was his wish to leave and it was her right to take him with her. The day she came, my mate's face lit up the sky. I was happy for him but I soon began to realise I was about to lose my lifetime friend. His mum seemed very nice. When I first met her, I was puzzled because she was white. This made me think about Markie's complexion. Then when I was introduced to his two older brothers, who were also white-skinned, I became even more confused.

As the days passed, I felt his departure getting closer. I kept a brave face, but inside I was hurting. I could sense him drifting away, no longer relying on me to look out for him and solve his problems. I knew I was going to miss him, right from the first day. Now I was feeling real loneliness. I asked Dotty to hurry up and find my real family. I wanted to leave, just like Markie.

It had been nearly seven months now and we were still keeping in touch. He had returned to Derby, where his mother had a house. It was mid-May and I remembered it would soon be his birthday. I'd made a request that Dotty allow me to phone him. She'd agreed and, as I stood in the main office under her watchful eye, for the third time that day, I listened to the buzz of the engaged phone. We didn't know at the time but the line had been disconnected. All this, and the fact that I was still at 521, was the reason for my present disruptive state of mind.

'I'm pissed off. I'm pissed off!' I'd learnt that from Danny Hawksley. I was now regularly telling the other kids to piss off as well. I'd also learnt it was cool to say the fuck word but I hadn't used it around 521 too loudly yet.

I'd changed the music and was playing Marc Bolan. My imaginary guitar was out, along with my straight, shoulder-length, blonde hair. Jumping about, imagining I was the lead singer, the sweat poured from me as I let off my frustration. It never crossed my mind for one minute that I was always imitating being white. The fact was I knew nothing about being black. With no role model I was lost. I talked white, ate white, walked white and danced white. In fact, I even dreamt white. Our different races and the colour of our skins, were never topics for discussion at 521. I guess this was another blunder attributable to trying to raise us in a perfect world. Discovering the real world was a far from perfect experience for most of us, having lived our lives cocooned in a well-financed, children's home.

I was one confused young man. I remember the day John Mac called me 'blacky' and got away with it. I hated him even more but would, nevertheless, attempt to help him when a force of evil descended upon 521 Aigburth Road.

The Black Prince of Terror

It was Friday, the thirteenth of June. We were all off school and dozing around the playroom, except the three girls and Hawksley. The girls were watching television in the main living room. Danny was still out somewhere with his mates from school. He went to Quarry Bank, as did the other coloured boys I knew who lived around there. They came from another home situated on Aigburth Hall Road. It was called Springwood and was run by Social Services. We were threatened that if we didn't behave, we'd be sent there. We were run by a private charity, therefore a class above them, or so we thought. We often met them at Christmas parties that were held by workers from major car factories and social clubs.

The two McPhersons and myself were playing the Home's new board game, 'Cluedo'. Davy Green, who was home for the holiday break, was wrestling on the floor with Girlie Boy. It must have been about six o'clock when the first drops of rain began to fall.

'No, Patrick lad, it wasn't Mrs. White and it wasn't in the living room,' I informed him. 'Your go, Graham!' I was having to shout over the sound of the stereo and the grunts coming from John Mac and Davy Green.

'Hey Davy, stop fighting and put the lights on!' I demanded. 'It's getting too dark.'

A large black cloud that had been in the distance a while ago, was now blocking out the remaining daylight. The rain had begun to fall heavily, thumping against the windows. Davy, not wanting to release his hold on John, began to drag him with him towards the light switch. I was surprised Girlie Boy allowed Davy to fling him to the floor these days, knowing the way he was.

Suddenly, the whole room lit up as if a giant torch was shining directly through the window. It lit up the whole sky before plunging us back into darkness. Young Patrick stood up. His brother Graham's eyes had opened wider than ever before as he stared towards the sky. Despite the howling wind and rain, the whole world seemed silent; silent and waiting.

Ka-boom! Our whole world exploded as the first roll of thunder crashed over us. Both young McPhersons jumped behind the big sofa.

'Turn the light on, Davy!' shouted Girlie Boy. But Davy had frozen by the light switch. The wind was beginning to fling things around the front garden. Waste paper, leaves and anything weightless, was being thrown against the windows. The rain began to hammer loudly at the thin panes of glass. From where I was sitting, the windows looked like they'd crash in on us at any moment

'Davy, the light mate, the light!' I pleaded. Just then, the room was lit up again by the flash of light from the sky and I saw Davy drop to the floor and scramble toward the sofa.

Ring! Ring! Ring! It was the front door.

There was a loud clap, that seemed to shake the whole house. Patrick began screaming and was momentarily joined by all of us as the door flew open.

'Is everyone okay?' It was Aunty Gwen, closely followed by the three girls. 'Don't touch the light, they've all blown. Aunty Dotty and Julie are sorting them out!'

Ring! Ring! The front doorbell continued to ring wildly, adding to the commotion inside the room. Patrick and Graham were both crying behind the sofa.

'Look after the young ones, girls, I'll have to answer the door! Everyone stay in here, and remember, don't turn the lights on!'

As the door closed, the sky lit up, this time quickly followed by the double flash of lightning and deep rumble of thunder. I could hear the metal bin lids, crashing on the concrete, at the side of the house. It must have been a sign but we didn't know it yet. The door bell had stopped ringing. I moved towards the playroom door. I was sure it must have been Danny, who'd be drenched by now. I stood with the door wedged open enough to see down the hallway and to the main front door. I could hear strangers' voices as greetings were being made. The porch door opened and I could make out Gwen in the dark. There were also three other figures entering the hallway behind her.

'Yes, we were expecting you. I must apologise, we've been plunged into darkness, not for long we hope. Please take your coats off.' It was dark but I could just about make out the figure of a kid with them. The other two were adults. Davy Green now joined me, watching the surprise visitors.

'Who are they?'

'I don't know!' Their coats were off and Gwen was guiding them towards the main office. As they disappeared behind the closing door, the hallway lit up. Power had been restored to 521.

'Put the light on!' ordered Zelda, which I'd done before she'd completed her sentence.

'Hey, it's a new kid, I think!' I was right, it was a new kid but we didn't get to meet him until suppertime. He was the blackest person I'd ever seen. I was staggered at how dark his skin was. He made me look mixed-race, like Markie. He told us he was from Africa. That his father was the king of a tribe in Nigeria, therefore, he was a prince. On first meeting him, I noticed something he did, I don't think anyone else saw. He was smiling as the other kids gathered around him but there was something about the smile. He was wearing a dirty, string-vest that hung below a red sweater which was too small for him. I looked at his matted hair that was badly in need of an Afro pick. His charcoal-black skin was dry and crusty, the lips cracked and sore-looking. He was in bad need of a hot bath and a good oiling. But what I found more off-putting was the ball of snot dangling from his nostrils. It looked like it had been there for days. Wet snot on dry snot. He was a mess.

'My name's Rakim Wasswarrior Matumbi Assifa, Prince of the Massifawarrior tribe', he snorted, swaying slightly from side to side.

He was thirteen, which made him the same age as Danny, Katy and me. As he finished informing us of his age, I noticed him grow in stature – just for a second. Then he seemed to shrink back to normal size, right in front of us. I don't think anyone else noticed. I continued watching him as he spoke to the other kids. John Mac was going out of his way to be liked, the way he did.

'Boy, you look like you need hosing down outside!' I thought to myself.

Suddenly, I saw the most perfect set of ivory white teeth

appear from his dark mouth. He looked directly at me with his head cocked to one side. I returned the gaze but he broke it off almost immediately. It was enough to send a warning signal to my basic instincts.

'Uh, oh! I don't think I like you.' I began to frown to myself.

As they all sat and ate supper in the kitchen, I withdrew to the playroom. I put on my one and only ska record. It was a parting gift from Markie; 'Wake up in the morning, slaving for breakfast,' Desmond Decker. However, my thoughts right now were on the fire I'd seen in that pair of eyes. Eyes reminiscent of an angry adult. Cruel, cold, cunning eyes. The new boy, the Prince of Matumbi. I began to shiver as my thoughts moved to Frank and Sheila Purdy.

Disturbances

On the new boy's first night, we all went to bed early and, unusually, straight to sleep. Black Prince Rakim occupied Markie's old bed. Davy, Danny and Girlie Boy McPherson, didn't even do their 'Waltons' routine as they frequently did.

'We will learn to behave, won't we?'
'Yes, Frank.'
'Now bend down! No, no, right down!'
'But, Daddy Frank, I'm sorry, I'm sorry, it was just water!'
'Too late now, I told yer not to spill it!'
'But, but'
'Pants to your ankles, yer know the routine. Down … down, quickly, or you'll regret it even more, I tell yer!'
'I'm sorry F-Frank, I'm sorry.'
Just as the memory of the pain about to be inflicted on me was played out, my eyes opened. I could feel the sweat beginning to form on my forehead. The room was completely dark and all I could hear was snoring coming

from Danny and Davy, or so I thought. I was about to sit up, when the movement caught my eye. I stopped as still as I could. Flashbacks of a recent ghost movie began to give me goose pimples.

'What was it?' It looked like a dark figure standing almost stock still. Right there, right beside Girlie Boy's bed. Was it Girlie Boy? What was he doing? Na, too tall to be him.

My battle to find a quick solution to what was making me sweat with fear, urged me to look to see if anyone else was out of their bed. My eyes slowly scanned the dark room. The real fear of spooking the ghostly figure into attacking me meant I couldn't take my eyes off it for too long. I looked at Markie's bed first and remembered he'd left us ages ago. I could see Davy's shape. I could hear Danny snoring. Then who was? Shit, I'd forgotten the new boy. The new boy! Markie's bed's empty. It's him, it's him!

I almost sprang up with excitement at my detective work but that would be careless. What was he doing? I decided to watch him. He stood beside McPherson's bed, almost in a trance. He seemed almost invisible, blending in with the night. 'How has he done that, how?' I turned over to lie on my side mimicking the sleeping movements I'd observed in the others. Suddenly, Girlie Boy began to move, spooking the shadow. I'd seen it on television I think, someone floating and now I saw this black shape gliding across our carpet. In the blink of an eye he was back in bed as if he hadn't moved.

My breathing pattern had altered for the fourth time since I'd woken so abruptly. My breathing became shallow. My bed clothes were drenched in sweat. I'd escaped from an old, recurring, bad dream only to wake and find a different kind of nightmare.

Maybe it was because John hadn't been attacked or, seemingly, troubled by the strange behaviour of Prince Weirdo Matumbi, that I had decided not to say anything for now. That Saturday morning I overslept because I'd been trying to make sure he didn't repeat his strange activity by my bed. I began to feel an early morning yawn coming, telling my body it was time to wake. I began to stretch out, rolling in the comfort of the freshly-scented sheets and pillow. The new day's light began to penetrate my eyelids, forcing me to prize them open. It was a new day.

It wasn't until I turned over to see who else was still in bed, that I saw him. He was awake, sitting on the edge of his bed looking at me. I smiled over in a friendly gesture. He slowly nodded his head at me. I felt as though I'd done something against him already. His eyes were almost boring into my skull, making me feel very uneasy.

I could see that most of the others, including Girlie Boy, had already gone down for breakfast but I was relieved to see that Davy was still in bed. I shut our strange new room mate out by closing my eyes. Turning my back on him, I could still feel his stare burning into me. I began to sense a very bad vibe about Prince Rakim Wasswarrior Matumbi Assifa.

Terror from Within

'Reverend Green in the study?' asked Zelda.

'No,' replied Danny, 'your go, Susan.' The game was drawing to an end. Most of us were playing except Girlie Boy McPherson and Rakim. The Black Prince of Matumbi was upstairs somewhere. I couldn't help noticing that Girlie Boy had been looking depressed all day. Shy Katy brought the game to an end by knocking the board off the table. It was an accident and a new game was about to be started,

'I'm going to the bog!' I informed everyone.

'Hurry up or yer out,' said Susan.

'I'm going for a shit, so!'

'We really wanted to know that, thank you very much,' scoffed Zelda.

'Johnny boy, you play in my place,' I suggested, moving towards the door.

'Na, I don't wanna.'

Just as I reached the door it opened. It was him. I nodded and smiled as I moved past him, into the hallway.

'A'right?' He nodded his head, which I took to mean that he was.

The best toilets in the house were upstairs. So that's where I headed. This would allow me to have a cigarette in safety. After I'd flushed the butt down the enamel bowl along with the day's diet, I closed the window, having made sure no evidence had been left. I slowly opened the door, just in case a staff member was snooping about. It wasn't until I reached the top of the stairs that I heard the voices from below. I stopped my descent to listen in.

'But!'

'No buts, you do what I say, remember!'

'Yes, but you said after!'

'Well, I've changed my mind, so, come on!' It was him, him and Girlie Boy and they were mounting the stairs. Dodging back, I scuffled down the corridor and into our bedroom. Quietly closing the door, I could hear the first set of feet reaching the top of the staircase. Quick, hide. Where shall I hide? The bed, yeah, Davy's. That's where I slid, under Greeny's bed, just as the door opened.

'Come on, there's no one here, hurry up.'

'Okay, okay, but…'

'What have I said about that word? I hate it, don't say it again!'

'Okay, Rakim,' came the submissive voice of John McPherson. I was trying to see through the space between the carpet and the counterpane. Without giving myself away, all I could see was their feet. It sounded like Girlie Boy was in trouble.

Suddenly, the Dunlop trainers disappeared from the carpet. The sound of the straining bed springs told me Girlie Boy had been pushed onto one of the beds.

'You will do what I fuckin' say, from today, White Finger!' I heard scuffling sounds and took the chance of lifting Greeny's bed cover which was obscuring my view.

'Yes, yes, okay, I'll do it, after.'

'You'd best not be lying, I tell yer and don't fucking tell anyone else, right?' He had Girlie Boy in some kind of armlock. I ducked back behind the cover.

'No, I won't say anythin' to anyone honest, honest!'

'You say, "Honestly, Prince Warrior Assifa". Go on!'

'Honestly, Prince Warrior Assifa.'

'Now, get up!' No sooner had Girlie Boy been let loose, than I saw his Dunlop trainers heading quickly towards the door.

'Hey, I never said you could go yet!' taunted the voice of the new terror. But Girlie Boy had sensed his chance to escape and wasn't stopping. Rakim moved after him as the door crashed open. That's when I heard the scream; a high-pitched scream.

On hearing the second set of feet reach the corridor outside the door, I rolled out from under the bed. Prince Terror had just disappeared into the hallway and the door swung shut behind him. By the sound of things, Johnny Boy had made good his escape. I had to get out of the room but as my hand touched the door knob, it opened and there he stood. He was smiling but it wasn't a smile, it was just a show of teeth; an aggressive show of teeth. Somehow, he'd stepped in and managed to close the door with his back to it. I wasn't smiling, because the new kid, who had just screamed like a banshee, was now looking really evil. I shied away as he spat out words at me.

'Oh! You again, Robbie Suilerman. Sounds Ibo? You are African, aren't you? What tribe?'

'I'm not African,' I replied.

'Ha, you're not? Then where yer from?'

'I dunno, I'm from here, just here!' I began to feel awkward. He was probing me and I didn't like it, or him.

'So, where have you just come from then?'

'What?'

'You heard me!' he smiled again. 'You was here a minute ago, weren't yer?' It was my turn to smile.

'What?'

'You're quite smart at that, aren't yer?'

'Smart at what?'

'Watching, you know, that's twice in what, forty-eight hours. You best watch yerself, I tell yer!' He stepped aside, as if he'd finished with me and I could now leave.

That's exactly what I did. I heard him grunt as I passed him but I ignored it. I didn't know how to handle this guy.

In fact, I didn't think I could handle him. I'd seen him behaving strangely since the day he'd arrived and hadn't forgotten seeing him floating across the bedroom floor. Reaching the playroom door, I could hear all the others laughing as they played but I turned round and headed for the garden. I was surprised to see Girlie Boy sitting on the large wooden tree stump beside the den and I walked over and stood beside him. He looked like he'd been crying.

'What's up, lad?' I asked tactfully.

'Nothing, nothing. It's cold, I'm going in.' With that, he stood up and smiled but it wasn't a smile I'd seen before from John Mac. I watched as he plodded off down towards the kitchen door.

'Shit! What's going on?' I asked myself. 'He said something about 'after'. McPherson has to do something for him 'after', he said, I wonder what?' As I stood deep in thought, Zelda appeared at the back door. She was coming out for a smoke as usual. Should I tell her what I think is going on?

Hidden Agenda

I decided not to say anything to Zelda about the things I'd observed. Something was going to happen that night. I was sure of that. I'd been watching John all through tea. He looked stressed and I was beginning to feel sorry for him.

After we'd eaten and been excused from the table by Dotty, I decided to go out for the rest of the evening, having received permission to go to my friend's house in Grassendale. I soon forgot about the trouble brewing at 521.

Getting my silver chopper out of the garage, I saddled up in preparation for my downhill ride towards Otterspool and Grassendale. This was a bike journey I enjoyed. It was the coming back I hated. I would always try and talk my new best mate Jonesy into riding back halfway on his bike. I'd made friends with Alan Jones at school. He was a late-starter as his family had not long moved into the area. Despite being in a different class from me, we seemed to admire something in each other. He lived with his mum, dad and two younger brothers.

As I reached the gates of Grassendale Park, I stopped to allow a vehicle to pass through. This was where he lived. It was a private park and said so on a large sign on the iron gate. There was even an old sentry box, empty now, positioned on the pavement beside the gate. Alan told me it was once used to stop riff raff getting in and that a man was employed to stand duty inside it. Riff raff, like the boys from Springwood, I thought.

'Hey, you'd best get yer dad to employ another sentry,' I told my mate. I'd seen some of the Springwood boys on their way to Otterspool Prom, which wasn't far away.

It was his mum who answered the back door to me. She was a nice lady, who always treated me well. I always used the back door. Not that I couldn't use the front, but that was the door my mate used, so I did likewise.

'Hey Al, that new boy, the African, he's putting McPherson under pressure over something.'

'Oh, the one that floats and walks round with a snotty nose?'

'Yeah him, Matumbi, he's deffo a loony!'

'What's he up to then?'

'I d' know, I asked Girlie Boy but he's scared, I think.'

'Scared of him? Where's Davy Green? He can take him on, can't he?'

'Even Davy's kind of wary of him. He ain't said so but I can sense it.'

We were up in the loft above his garage. His old man used to work in a scrap yard and had a garage to store his junk or, as his mum used to call it, 'that effin' junk!'

'Shit, Al, what time is it?' We'd been talking for what seemed like hours. I had to be back home by nine o'clock.

'It's nearly five past nine.' He knew he'd made me stay too long. Now I'd have to ask his mum to phone and explain why I'd be late.

'A puncture, yes, they're fixing it now. Okay, thanks, bye.' That was the first excuse we could think of. I now had an extension to stay out until 9.30. Alan's mum was going to walk part of the way with me to make sure I made it safely to Aigburth Road.

It was nearly 9.40 by the time I arrived back at 521. Dotty was waiting for me at the gate with one of her stern looks but she didn't get on my case. Most of the others were in bed, which I found comforting.

Big Zelda was in the kitchen having her supper. I'd been told to get my hot drink and toast eaten sharpish, so as not to disturb the other lads who would be sleeping. My pyjamas had been brought down and I was to get ready for bed in the bathroom.

'Hey Zel, what d'yer think of our African Prince then?' I asked, placing my hot drink and plate of toast beside her at the table.

'Well, he seems alright I suppose, he gets on okay with John Mac.'

'What makes you say that, Zel?'

'They've been together all evening!'

'So, John Mac wasn't upset?'

'Why, should he be?'

'No, I'm just asking.'

'Come on now, Robbie, time to get changed and up to bed.' Dotty was calling from the dining room hatch into the kitchen.

'Yeah, I'm going now,' I replied.

Well, at least I could have a smoke in my favourite bathroom upstairs. It must have been late now. The latest I'd ever stayed up, anyway. Passing our bedroom door, I thought about the lads inside. They'd probably be sleeping by now. Except Rakim. I had a feeling he'd be awake.

'Hey, don't you be all night in that bathroom!' said Dotty 'and you can stop smoking in there, as well!' She seemed to have the knack of knowing everything. I came out of the bathroom and caught sight of her heading towards the stairs.

'Come on, into bed.'

'Good night, Aunty.'

'Good night, young man.'

I waited by the bedroom door and listened to her going

downstairs. The lights were out in our room but I had a good sense of where I was going. It was very quiet. I should have been on my guard but I wasn't as I was grabbed from behind.

Unnatural Behaviour

I didn't shout out at my sudden attacker, who was joined by two of the other occupants who shared the bedroom, even as I was propelled towards my bed at the far end of the room. It was just the lads having a joke, or so I thought. For a second, I hadn't realised that the new boy was also part of the ambush. There were three of them. I knew I had Davy and Danny pinning me down. Someone else had grabbed hold of my legs. It was him. I began to struggle now but it was hopeless and I felt the weight of someone sitting on my lower back.

'Hey, fuck off! Fuck off, you lot, stop messin'!' I began to plead.

'Gag him! Gag him! Hurry up!' It was his voice. He was in charge. I really began to panic now. I'd left it too late. I could smell a sweaty hand being placed around my mouth.

'D-Davy, st-stop! Stop!' They were the last muffled words I spoke before my pyjama top ripped. A sudden cold hit my upper body, as the remainder of my top was dragged from my body and tossed into the dark. My lungs began to scream behind the sweaty palm over my mouth.

'Hold him tight, I mean, really tight!' I felt the armlock that Davy had placed me in.

I was desperately trying to move now, but I couldn't. For a moment I gave up. The punch aimed at my kidneys hurt and inside I screamed but my torture was far from over. One of my attackers had placed his arm about my neck. I was frightened now, really frightened. Someone was punching me about my back. I felt an open-handed slap to my bare skin. This sent a shock of pain through my whole body. The large hand, which must have left an imprint, began to grab hold of the elastic supporting my underpants. He was laughing. I could hear the wicked intentions inside his laugh. The elastic began to tighten around my waist, as he attempted to lift me off the bed by my briefs. As I was already pinned down by Davy and Danny, his task was impossible. I felt them rip and it was then that he began to pull at them like a wild animal.

'Help, help me! Help!' I screamed into the hand that was still covering my mouth. I was almost stark-naked. The cold air hit my legs, as the last piece of clothing was torn from me. Someone was still punching me. My stomach had gone tense. My lungs were hurting as I attempted to scream.

I called it the finger because that's what I thought it was. The person standing behind me began to slap me hard before pushing his 'finger' between my buttocks. Inside, I screamed. Inside, my whole world went dark. It was the place I called my waste disposal, and it was being invaded. The whole room began to spin round. A sickness came at the back of my throat but the hand clamped to my mouth prevented it leaving. He took it out and pushed it in again. I was going to kill him. I was going to kill all of them.

Bang! I heard the loud crash of the door before the light hit my eyes. The sudden release of pressure on my body caused me to drop to the carpet.

'What is going on here?' It was Dotty Crystal's voice. By now, I'd nearly crawled beneath the bed. My eyes were shut tight and I curled into a ball.

'Okay, you three, down to my office now! Wait for me outside.' I heard them scampering out of the room. Dotty then told Girlie Boy McPherson, who I presume had watched the whole procedure, to go downstairs. I gritted my teeth, as I heard the shuffle of her slippers approaching the bed. I'd now crawled completely underneath. I could hear more adults entering the room. They began to talk.

'Please, you watch them downstairs, I'll see what's happened. Where are his pyjamas?'

'This looks like them here.' It was Aunty Gwen and Dotty. I heard one of them leave, before the voice started talking to me. But I wasn't talking. I didn't feel like talking.

'Robbie, come on, come out of there. Come and put your 'jamas back on.' It was Dotty, trying to coax me out.

In the end, she left my ripped pyjamas and went downstairs. I wasn't coming out. Not for her anyway. Hearing her footsteps descending the stairs, I grabbed my torn pyjamas. After putting them on as best as I could, I crawled out from under the bed and climbed into the warmth of the blankets. I was crying silently, I don't quite know when I started shaking.

It was Gwen who came back. They knew I liked Gwen. She sat on the edge of the bed. I smelt her perfume and began to cry again. She asked me what had happened. I looked at her. She had brown, curly, shoulder-length hair. Her eyes were green and they were asking, concerned eyes, but my words just wouldn't come. I closed my eyes and shook my head.

'Nothing, nothing,' I muttered, as I turned my back and continued crying.

'Robbie, you can come and sleep in the sick room tonight. How about that?'

'Just fuck off an' leave me alone!' That was the first time I'd ever sworn at an adult. Gwen said it was alright to swear when you were angry and had been hurt. She was still trying but soon gave up. I wasn't going to talk about it, I just wished Markie was here. He'd remember. He'd know what the pain was like.

Markie had also felt pain. We'd never talked to anyone else about those things. We'd bottled them up. It was all a living nightmare. A nightmare that should have stopped when we came to 521. But I was on my own and, to my horror, the nightmare had begun again. I knew the perpetrator was Rakim this time but he was the same as Fat Frank. I was crying. Gwen was rocking me in her arms.

I don't know what time the others returned to the bedroom. I woke up in the sick room. It was Sunday, I knew that. I hadn't been awake long before the door opened and Gwen appeared with a large tray of breakfast in her hands.

'I thought you'd like this,' she said, placing the tray on

the bedside cabinet. She then moved towards the curtains that were still drawn. I could smell her perfume again. 'I hope you feel better this morning?'

That was her first question but I knew it wasn't going to be the last. It didn't take her long to reach the subject of what had taken place that night. I asked her where she bought her perfume and she smiled at me, knowing I was avoiding any questions today. She sat with me while I ate my breakfast but my appetite wasn't there. Feeling sick again, I told Gwen I wasn't hungry and she left to return the tray to the kitchen.

'You have a long rest in today,' she suggested as she reached the door. The sick room was quiet and I closed my eyes again. Inside my head it was black but then it went red and I felt myself going cold from my feet to my forehead. My arms could not move, as though someone had glued them to the mattress. I was stuck.

'W-what's happening now? Where's Gwen? Help! Help!' My head refused to move. I was trying to shout her name but the words weren't coming out. I felt like a lead weight. All I could move was my eyes. I realised I was still breathing by the condensation that began to appear as I exhaled. It had gone colder now but I was sure the window was closed. Or was it open? Had Gwen..? No, she wouldn't leave it open.

'I can't see, I can't move, I'm paralysed, I'm … Help! … Help, somebody help!' I screamed inside my mind. My bones began to shudder as my temperature continued to drop.

It wasn't a loud knock. More like a tapping but I was relieved to hear it. I still couldn't move or speak. Whoever it was would have to use their instincts and just enter the room. They were still tapping outside the damn door. I wanted to scream so they would hear me. I sighed with relief when I heard the sound of the door handle click open. Someone was there, I heard the door close behind them but I still couldn't see who had come to my rescue. It was still cold and whoever it was still hadn't spoken yet. It wasn't Gwen, I would have smelt her perfume by now. The footsteps began to shuffle towards the bed. My eyes had moved to the corner of their sockets in a vain attempt to see who it was. At that point, my nose was invaded by the most disgusting smell I'd sensed in my short life. I immediately began to retch from the pit of my stomach. Nothing came up.

Suddenly, hands appeared. They were large, dark hands. They were his hands.

'What's happening to me? Help! Help!' I silently screamed. Again, nothing came out. The evil face of the new boy shot in front of my watery vision. It was his breath I could smell as he entered the room. His face was only inches from mine and the smell became unbearable.

His sick, evil grin was like a mask of tortured ebony. My arms and legs were trying desperately to move but they refused. Rakim's evil eyes had turned black, blacker than his skin. His pupils glowed red. My screams were loud, yet silent to the outside world. This was some kind of voodoo.

Purdy

I didn't know how he'd got inside the sick room. I couldn't understand it but the black beast still stood over me. Evil Matumbi smelt of something ungodly. He placed the ends of his fingers into my eye sockets. The mucus that constantly discharged from his nostrils, began to dribble onto my forehead. He was laughing; a mad, high-pitched laugh. I was being blinded by a raving lunatic. I could hear the sound of eye muscle and bone giving way. The pain was real, he was pushing my eyeballs to the back of my skull.

Suddenly, the door crashed open and I heard the sound of footsteps. My attacker paused but I could still feel his snot dripping onto my skin. The heavy footsteps stopped. That's when I smelt the toiletbrush aftershave. The one he always wore for her.

'Purdy! It's Purdy. Markie, he's coming! He's coming!'

Matumbi now began to flatten my nose bone by using his

own. The warm, salty, yellow balls of snot began to run onto my top lip and he was howling like a psychotic wolf. Now I felt a new attacker, forcing my legs apart. I was screaming. It was happening all over again.

'You've been a naughty bad, bad boy again, ain't yer?' came the nightmare voice of Fat Frank Purdy.

'No, Frank! No Frank, I've been a good boy!'

Rakim was still howling and had begun to sink his teeth into my neck. I began to howl as well but his was pleasure mine was pain.

Purdy's gross, fat body was weighing down on me. Inside my heart gave way. My mind was exploding with flashing lights. My screams were loud, my lungs under stress.

'Help! Help! God feel my pain, please hear my scream! Help!'

My body was rigid and suddenly began to shudder. I was moving. My right leg pulled free of the sweaty grip on my ankle. Realising I could move, I pulled my left arm from the mattress and began to lash out. I saw light now. Lots of light shining into my face. There was a voice, another, kind voice but my body was still being restrained. It was a trick. The kind voice was just a trick and I began to kick out wildly.

Again I screamed but this time I felt and heard it coming out. I inhaled in preparation to let off another wail, when the smell struck me. It was a sweet smell, a smell that immediately made me halt. The voice was back. The kind voice. I knew whose voice it was.

'Shush, shush, everything's okay Robbie, you can stop now. It's okay, I'm here and you're safe.' It was Gwen. The lids of my eyes, that I had assumed had been open, now parted. I was in a large white room. There were other people there, all staring at me. I was lying on an unfamiliar leather sofa. The warm hands that had held my arms and legs let go. I began to look around and was sure I wasn't in any room at 521. I was wet with sweat and drained of energy. My first request, when I realised the situation was real, was for water. I needed to know where I was and soon realised it was the local doctor's surgery in Garston Old Road.

Gwen went on to explain that I had woken up the whole

house by screaming in the middle of the night. All attempts to wake me had been fruitless. My body was rigid and my temperature had risen dramatically. Real questions were going to be asked. I could see Dotty Crystal over Gwen's shoulder. She was in deep conversation with Dr. Swayze, our doctor; Markie's and mine. Markie ... I began to cry again thinking of my friend out there on his own. Was he also having nightmares?

'You kept mentioning the name Purdy, Robert, why is that?' The question came from the other side of the room. It was J. R. Fuller, the boss of the Home. I wasn't about to talk to him and I don't think they expected me to either. He was just preparing the ground for his staff. The name of my night-time terror was known and they'd want to talk about it.

'Yes, you fucking twat!'
'Twat? What is a twat?'
'You are. Now piss off, prick!'
This guy was a real fool and I had to put up with him for another two weeks. All the way out here in the middle of nowhere. We were in Angelsey. I'd been sent away on a holiday and although Aunty Gwen had come with me, so had this fool. His name was Antoine; he was some kind of psychotherapist and was constantly getting on my tits.

'I know what, Antoine. Why don't you show me how to climb that large rock over there, the dangerous-looking one!'
'Now Robert, that isn't being nice. Remember Mr. Nice?'
'How the fuck can I remember Mr. Nice, when all day I have to put up with you? And me name's Robbie. Okay?'
'Okay, Robbie Suilerman. Yes, that sounds fine to me!'
'Listen tit face. Who gives a toss what you think, just fuck off, I know what you do so leave me alone!'
After saying all I had to say to Antoine, which was a lot more than the day before, I stormed off towards the cottage. Gwen would be cooking an evening meal. The cows watched me from the field as I walked by. They stank. Worst of all was their noise. I could never live out here I thought. I could hear silly Antoine trying to catch up to me.

I wanted to go home, back to 521 Aigburth Road. I

couldn't even remember what had really happened anymore. Was it all a nightmare? Deep down, I knew it wasn't but which parts were and which parts weren't? I was confused; I was alone and hurting. I looked towards the sky and prayed I could die without pain. I hated pain.

Antoine caught up with me as I fell to the ground and silently wept. He said it was alright to cry. I told him to fuck off again. He wouldn't, he just kept talking. He said he understood.

It was dark by the time I'd stopped crying. Antoine had managed to cover me with his jacket and sat a few yards away from me. The grass was feeling damp and the night began to seep in.

'Come on, I'll race you!' I shouted, jumping to my feet and gaining a head start on him. He was pretty fast for an old man but with my head start, no contest for me. I was also beginning to put on weight. Gwen said I was eating more due to the country air. She didn't know about my stash. The chocolate bars and crisps that I stored away in my bedroom to stuff myself with at twelve o'clock. I was eating for comfort and thought I'd get away with it for the whole four weeks but Antoine got onto me; that was his job. We talked a lot in the last week and we left as friends. Antoine was a black man and my first ever role model. Following that holiday I began to imitate Antoine Rodgers.

As we drove over the Menai Bridge on our return to Liverpool, I closed my eyes and wished they'd hurry up and find my real family, if I had one. I also prayed the wicked Rakim Wasswarrior Matumbi Assifa had been killed while I was away.

Revenge

He seemed to explode for no reason. The Prince was losing control. Not that I gave a shit anyway. In fact, I did my damnedest to create situations that would result in him going into one of his fits. Sheila Purdy used to have them, so it was befitting that he was having them too but he was worse. The destruction he caused was horrific.

I had been back for two weeks since my month away in Wales. The only person I spoke to was Girlie Boy McPherson, who'd rushed out to carry my suitcase for me. I think he felt really sorry for me, even after all the things I had done to him. I'd have to change my ways a little.

I'd just arrived back from Jonesy's house in Grassendale and was putting my chopper into the garage. John Mac came flying around the corner with the fear of God in his face. I wasn't surprised when Rakim came hot on his heels.

'Fuckin' come here, you. Fuckin' get here!' he ranted, as he tried to catch his breath. Girlie Boy began to circle me and my bike, to stay out of Rakim's reach. Matumbi was beginning to foam about the mouth with anger. That's when Dotty appeared with Aunty Julie and Gwen.

'Rakim, stop this now, stop it. John stand still or come to me', pleaded Dotty but John couldn't hear. He was running for dear life. Rakim was out for blood as usual and just ignored everyone. He stopped in front of me as Girlie Boy stopped behind me. That's when I saw the kitchen knife Rakim was wielding and when it registered that I alone stood between Rakim and his prey.

I didn't make a habit of lifting my chopper to head height. Somehow it reached that position before dropping down on a gasping Wassifa. He moved quickly. The bike crashed down on the concrete drive. I was horrified that I'd missed him but when I saw him lose his balance and fall over the stack of spare bike wheels and the knife slip from his hand, I felt I would survive the storm. Aunty Gwen bounced on him, quickly followed by Julie and Dotty. He was spitting and cursing like a devil from hell. The three adults were finding it hard to contain him when, for the third time that week, Mary the cook – who weighed about fourteen stone – entered the arena.

'Where's my kitchen knife? Oh yes, I'd better sit on this one again!' she said, pushing herself between Gwen and Dotty. I heard the stuffing blow out of Rakim as she plonked herself down on top of him. I looked at John Mac, who appeared mighty relieved that the Prince of Terror had been subdued.

'He called me a black bastard. He did, he fucking did!' screamed Rakim from underneath the cook.

'That's what yer are, though,' I thought silently to myself.

'And you, you Robbie Suilerman, you're fucking dead. I'll get you!'

'Robbie, you and John go into the house!' ordered Dotty, nodding towards Aunty Julie who was to return with us.

'Oh, I'm sorry, I'm sorry!' He'd switched tactics. He was attempting to play the sorry card.

He had been in this situation before in the dining room. Then he had pleaded remorse to Mary and Dotty, and that time they'd believed him, despite all the Home's broken china and glass display cabinet. He had smashed them to pieces in a storming fit. It was only when he'd finished that Dotty felt safe enough to approach him. I prayed, as I walked to the kitchen door, that they would sit on him all night. I was in big trouble unless something was done about Wasswarrior. As we walked into the kitchen, the other kids scrambled to the window to watch.

'All into the playroom, come on, there's nothing to see!' Julie reassured us.

'You alwight, John?' came the squeaky question from young Patrick. Girlie Boy's sister Susan and Graham also gathered round him to make sure he hadn't received any injuries.

It was at times like these that I missed Markie and Davy Green, who was still at boarding school. Danny Hawksley had the sense not to get too involved, he was infatuated with big Zelda and hardly ever spoke to Rakim. I'm not sure whether he was fully aware of Rakim's intentions the night he helped to hold me down. He kept going out of his way to try and make up to me but I had blanked out the whole incident. Therefore he got no response, because I also blanked him out.

My heart sank just before supper time when he walked into the playroom with one of his big grins across his face. Rakim Wasswarrior had talked his way out of trouble. I was so angry, I knew this would happen. We ate supper in silence. Everyone was there, even big Zelda. A funny kind of tension prevailed. Prince Rakim was in his element now. I watched the sly grins in my direction as he sipped his hot chocolate. I was in the mood for murder. I was scared and I was angry. How could grown-ups be so stupid? Were they doing this on purpose? Was it a game to them? I looked towards John McPherson's chair. He'd disappeared.

'Shit, where did Girlie Boy go?' I felt as though I was the only one who was really concerned about what was going on. Maybe it was my fault that the nightmare was continuing. I could have stopped it. I could have told them, told someone what he had done to me that night. But I didn't. Maybe I was too ashamed. Maybe I was waiting for my opportunity to get my revenge.

After supper, we all made our way upstairs. I was the first to leave and headed towards my bathroom. Nicotine was needed. The door should have been locked but wasn't. I didn't notice him until I'd locked the door and switched the light on. He was sitting in the bath. His pyjamas were still on and there was no water, except for the tears that were streaming down his face. That's when I first felt genuine sympathy for someone else. Girlie Boy McPherson sat there and covered his face with his hands and wept. I began to think about Antoine. I was going to have to play the psychotherapist. Moving to the edge of the bath, I placed my hand on the top of his head and began to speak.

'It's alright mate, it's alright to cry. I know what it's like, Johnny, I understand, it's okay!' I don't know where the words came from or why they came but the effect was almost immediate.

'I – I can't go in there with him, I can't, he's … he's evil!'

'Calm down first John, then tell me what's been going on. I know he's been plotting things with you!'

'No, I don't plot with him. He … he … oh … I … I!'

'Johnny, I know you remember what happened to me that night, so you don't have to fear telling me anything, I mean anything!'

'You swear not to tell a soul, Rob? Swear, first!'

'I swear I won't, unless you want me to tell. Okay?'

He'd told me the worst things I had to hear in the space of five minutes. I was burning inside. I used to hate this little spoilt white boy but I was being forced into feeling his pain. Hearing his cry. I didn't know how I was going to carry the burden of what he'd told me but I'd given him my word. I'd also sworn to see the end of Prince Rakim Wasswarrior Assifa Matumbi. I left the bathroom allowing McPherson time to clean his face up. I was surprised and relieved to see Gwen pulling up a chair beside the bedroom door as I approached. She would sit there until we were all asleep. This always happened when we'd been at war with each other. Rakim was already in bed with his back facing the wall as I walked past him to reach my bunk. The thought of the kitchen knife flashed through my mind and into his spine but Gwen was watching and the kitchen knife was locked away.

I was in tune with McPherson, we'd broken our animosity towards each other. Maybe it was his silent cry for my help that woke me. It was about five in the morning and I could hear the birds twittering outside. The daylight had managed to find a gap in the curtains and shone into the room. Turning from the window to face the door, my heart stopped. It was closed. The sentry had gone. When did she leave? She was supposed to watch us all night. Where's Rakim? To my horror his bed was empty and so was John Mac's. I scanned the room to make sure they weren't in there. They weren't. I began to sense something was going on. Johnny Boy was in trouble.

Slowly pushing back my blankets, I placed my bare feet onto the carpet. It was very quiet. Slipping my pumps and dressing gown on, I went to investigate the whereabouts of Rakim and Girlie Boy. Instinct told me to head for the bathrooms but they were both empty. I stood in the passageway trying to think of where they could possibly be. Suddenly, my feet were moving towards the stairs. I don't know why I was going downstairs but my feet were taking me. They started to slow down as I reached the playroom door. My sixth sense took over and told me to walk quietly. I was on my tip toes now. My senses told me that they were in there as I began to turn the door handle.

The Cottage

All the commotion had died down over the last three months but for some of us, the scars would remain deep. We were all happy to be away from the city, the pollution and the noise. Out here, the fresh country air blended with sea and salt and filled our lungs. At this precise moment, we were all on the beach, just us kids that is. We'd all decided to walk to the local shops. Nicotine levels were low. We had stopped to watch the crashing waves thundering towards us, the sea looked cruel. It could take life, we knew that, we had been warned. It was the chilly month of April showers, although it hadn't rained that day. It was cold and Anglesey wasn't known as the first place to see the summer sun.

We were all out here on a mini-holiday. Our schools had been informed and we'd been given special time out. We all needed a break from 521. Not only that but changes were being made. Painters and decorators were already at the house when we left. 521 was about to receive a major face lift, inside and out. We'd also been informed of a change in sleeping arrangements. The girls were being moved into our room. There was space for five people in there but big Zelda had refused to share again. She was therefore given the two young McPherson's room, next door to the sick room. I was to get my own room and so was Danny Hawksley. The three McPherson brothers would have to share Katy and Susan's old room connected to Danny's and my own. It was decided that Davy Green would sleep in the sick room when he returned for holidays.

We were all happy. Happy that he'd gone. I was at

Jonesy's house when they came for him. In fact, I'd been told to go out by Aunty Gwen. 'Make yerself scarce today,' she told me. Gwen and Aunty Julie had taken all the other kids to the pictures. Danny, I think, went out with his mates. It was all cloak and dagger stuff, which I guess it had to be, in order to catch Rakim unawares. He was permanently paranoid. None of us knew what was planned, but we knew something had to be done about him. We weren't surprised, more relieved and happy.

I took a large deep breath of sea air and looked at John Mac who was standing beside me. He was watching the mountainous waves, crashing towards the rocks.

'Yep!' I thought to myself, Girlie Boy had been looking much better of late, more relaxed. He was holding onto his younger brother, Graham. Patrick was with Susan and the others, further up the beach. I'd begun to take a liking to Susan Mac as well.

Girlie Boy began to smile at me. I'd forgotten I was staring at him. I returned my gaze to the roaring sea but my thoughts were still on Girlie Boy. The thoughts brought back the visions of what I'd seen taking place in the playroom that morning and the ordeal he had been put through. No one knew how long it had been going on. If I hadn't woken up and gone down to find him, his nightmare may still not have ended. I was now his hero and mentor, although I didn't want to be. Girlie Boy began to dog me everywhere I went. But, because I'd sensed his pain, I now made time for Johnny McPherson.

'I'm not going to the cave with them lot!' he said.

'Why not?'

'Are you?'

'Yeah!'

'Okay, I am then.' Everything I ate, he ate, everything I said, he said. He even wanted to perm his hair curly. I couldn't believe it. A white boy, who wanted to be black.

'Come on, let's go!' I suggested, moving off towards the others.

'Come on, let's go!' came my echo, repeating my words for the benefit of his brother Graham.

We all walked along the beach towards Aladdin's Cave

store, which was perched on a hill beside the main road. It was a real cave that had been converted into a huge shop, selling everything: sunbeds, buckets, spades, ice cream, hats, sun glasses, wind-breakers, beach balls, sweets and cigarettes. That's what we'd come for, cigarettes, and big Zelda was fronting for them. She was old enough to smoke anyway. We stood outside the store and smoked one each before we made our way back towards the cottage. This time Zelda suggested we use the main road for our return journey, instead of the beach. There wasn't a pavement or any street lights, like we were used to in the city, and it was getting dark. We trooped along the little footpath beside the road in single file. Occasionally, we were illuminated by the headlights of passing vehicles and eventually reached the old Welsh church. This was the dare of the evening; to pass the church graveyard. It wasn't until we reached halfway, that someone saw something.

'What's that, what's that?' Danny was pointing madly at the wall behind us.

'It's Rakim. It's Rakim!' shouted Zelda.

'Aa-Aargh!' Everyone was running down the hill towards the yellow light in the distance that was the cottage. Big Zelda cruelly ran off into the dark having deliberately caused the panic. Danny Hawksley had also disappeared. I could hear the two young McPhersons screaming at the rear. They were getting left behind and I knew I'd have to stop for them. Anyway, I was no longer afraid of Rakim Matumbi. Not anymore. I'd seen real fear in his eyes on the day I heard him plea for mercy and beg for my forgiveness. I'd refused to give him any. He was the Devil and I was going to beat him down.

That morning when I reached the playroom, I slowly opened the door. That's when I saw it. For the first time in my life, I was overpowered with rage. At first he hadn't noticed me. He was so engrossed in his devilry, he didn't know I'd crept up on him. Not until I struck him down with a wooden chair. He was completely naked and defenceless. I'd caught the devil off guard and I was going in for the kill. I caught sight of Girlie Boy's pyjamas and underwear tossed in the far corner and I could hear him sobbing somewhere behind me as I moved in on our tormentor.

Rakim had scuttled beside the stereo. This time he was going to die. My whole vision was coloured red including the Black Prince of Terror, whose hands were now outstretched, in a bid to defend himself. He tried to grab hold of the descending chair but it crashed down on his knuckles before halting with a thud on his bare knee caps. That's when he screamed and I wanted to hear it again. So I quickly raised my weapon and repeated the procedure. This time his skin split open. Seeing the crimson red liquid sent me into overdrive. The chair had broken. It now had dagger-like splinters in place of its wooden legs. As I brought the chair up, I saw them. They looked sharp. They would do, they would drive right through him.

I had to be quick, I could hear them coming. The adults. There was no way they couldn't hear this. Rakim's high-pitched screams would have woken his dead ancestors. I'd have to kill him fast. His hands were up again, he'd seen the deadly-looking weapon. Any fool could read my next move and, from the look on his face, he knew my intention. The skin on his legs was torn, blood running freely down his shins as I swung the daggers at him. His hands caught them and he screamed, a high-pitched, shrill scream. The wooden dagger had stuck right through the palm of his hand. I gritted my teeth and pulled. He screamed and I pulled harder.

The door crashed open. A large, clay flowerpot had found its way into my free hand. Girlie Boy had put it there. I raised it above Rakim. Dotty was now in the room. So was Gwen.

'No, Robbie, no, put it down!' came their demands. He was helpless and I was going to finish him off. I looked at Gwen, her eyes were pleading.

'He's not worth it, Robbie. Put it down!' My breathing was fast and heavy. I looked at Girlie Boy. His face was a mask of hate; hate for the boy I had at my mercy. I knew McPherson wanted me to smash the pot on his face.

'Don't, please don't!'

He began to plead for mercy. This made me even angrier. He didn't deserve any. Dotty was edging closer. I snarled at her, threatening to release the pot. She stopped and tried a tactful approach.

'Come on now, Robbie, this won't solve anything, will it?'

'Solve!' I yelled. 'Who wants to solve? I'm gonna kill him!' as the clay pot slipped from my fingers.

Sexuality

I don't know how she did it but somehow, Dotty managed to knock the falling pot off course, sending it smashing into the skirting boards.

Rakim had wet himself. The only sound following the deadly silence that ensued came from Girlie Boy. He was crying. I like to think that this was because the pot missed but I knew he was still in pain. I was glad Dotty had reacted as quickly as she did because if I'd done what I'd wanted to and smashed his face in, I knew I'd be in serious trouble.

We all made it back to the cottage safely. It was hot Ovaltine and muffins around the coal fire for supper. There was a telly but all the programmes were in Welsh. Since none of us spoke Welsh, we gave it a miss. John Mac was excited at the prospect of sleeping outside in the tent. Katy and his sister had been out there the last two nights. Now it was our turn. I wasn't really looking forward to the prospect of sleeping in a small tent with insects and field rats but if Girlie Boy was game, so was I. We had large, duck down sleeping bags that were already warmed by piping-hot water bottles.

'Yeah,' I thought 'sleeping in the wild will be an adventure.' The two girls had done it, so could we.

I looked at McPherson and wished Markie or Davy Green were here instead. Markie would have loved camping out. Danny Hawksley was no use to anyone except Zelda. She had him trained like a Zombie. He did everything she said and she had told him not to sleep outside with the bugs.

With the last dregs of Ovaltine gone, everyone began to make their way to bed.

'Torch!' shouted Girlie Boy, 'I need a torch!'

'Okay, John, don't panic,' replied Dotty from the back door. 'Now you two!' Next came the do's and don'ts which took her a whole five minutes to talk us through. After switching on our torches we began our journey across the damp grass towards the orange shape in the middle of the huge back garden.

'You go in, Johnny, I'm going for a piss..!'

To relieve myself, I had to trudge towards the bushes that separated the field next door. I began to think about Rakim and of how glad I was that he'd gone. It didn't take Dotty and her staff long to suss out what had happened this time. Johnny Boy had broken our code of silence. But no-one blamed him for it. I just wished I'd had the guts to tell when it happened to me. Girlie Boy also saved me from getting into trouble. I'd envisaged myself being shipped off to boarding school like Davy Green, until he spoke out. He had to tell, just as much as I had to come to his aid.

Twoo! Twooo!

'Shit, a fucking owl!' It made me piss down my leg, breaking me out of my trance. I scuffled towards the tent and nearly tripped over the guide ropes. I stooped down to enter into the orange walls of the two-man tent. McPherson was already inside his sleeping bag. Removing my overcoat, I unzipped my sleeping bag. The water bottle was still hot and the inside of the bag warm as my feet reached inside.

'Checked for any bugs, Rob?'

'Shit, no, shit!' Girlie Boy's reminder triggered one of my phobias; insects crawling on me. Just as I'd gone through the routine of checking the sleeping bag, it began to rain. I was glad of the tent walls as I jumped back into the duck feather bag.

'See yer in the mornin', Johnny'

'Yer goin' asleep already?'

'Yeah!'

'Can't we talk, just for a bit?'

'Alright, not for too long though, I'm tired!'

We talked for about an hour. Girlie Boy did all the asking,

me the talking.

'Yeah me an' Markie was lucky that day. If the fat man had been home, we'd have been in for his punishment.' I think I'd told him this story before. I always told people this story. 'Could you imagine that Johnny? Johnny ... John ...' As always, he'd fallen asleep and left me talking to myself. I could hear the wild sounds from outside in the night. It was still raining but the downpour had ceased, for now.

Twoo – twoo.

'Fucking owl!' I cursed, as I snuggled down inside my bag and turned off the torch light. The full day of activity out in the fresh air began to take its toll and I was soon sound asleep.

It must have been the sound of the early birdsong that woke me, and the urgent need to relieve myself meant leaving the tent. I knew it was cold out there but I was ready to burst. Outside, the mushrooms got crushed under my size nine Dr. Martens. It was misty as the dew began to rise from the ground. The sun was creeping over the hill to the east but it was still cold. I was still half asleep and again nearly tripped on the guide ropes as I stumbled back into the tent. McPherson was still asleep. I intended to return to the dream I was having. It was a nice dream but the nice dreams weren't like nightmares, I could never go back to a nice dream. Nightmares always restarted exactly where they left off. I hadn't had a nightmare for a long time.

The field of daffodils I was standing in were part of a new dream. I felt good. Warm. Different. The sun was shining directly in my face and I felt the warm rays moving towards my throat before heating up my chest. A sweet smell of flowers hit my nostrils. A breeze. The heat moved to my stomach, warming it inside, moving up and down my tense stomach muscles. I felt good. Suddenly, for some unknown reason, Zelda appeared from the daffodils. She was smiling at me. I knew it had to be a dream. She hadn't smiled at me like that since Markie and me first arrived at 521. Then she touched me the way she used to touch us and I began to feel good.

Zelda was laughing now. I shook myself awake but I wasn't in time to stop the explosion. I was sweating. The sleeping bag had rolled away from me somehow. Girly Boy's bag was empty, his wash bag and towel gone. He'd beaten me to the showers. Now I'd have to wait until he'd finished and I knew I'd wet myself although my sleeping bag felt dry. It was just my legs that felt sticky. I'd never felt like this before. I was relaxed. Really relaxed. I wanted it to happen all over again. I heard McPherson slamming the door to the showers.

It was our last day and we'd been promised a trip to Snowdonia that morning. We all had a good day, returning to the cottage quite late that evening. The new minibus was no longer new. It was caked in mud and someone had managed to scratch off three letters from the Dr. Barnado's logo printed on the side panels. Aunty Dotty was angry but I was pleased. Girlie Boy had nearly fallen down a rather steep hill, Danny and big Zelda had been caught necking behind a mountain shack and shy Katy was sick as we arrived. Other than that we had a good time and returned exhausted. Most of us ate supper and went straight to our bunks. It was an early start for all of us in the morning. I was dreading the long journey back to the city and having to help pack things away.

Johnny and me had to spend our last night in the tent. I'd managed to borrow Katy's little radio. I hoped this would block out the noise of the night creatures but I was so exhausted I was nearly asleep on my feet. I remember crawling into the tent and then into the sleeping bag. Girlie Boy was doing all the talking. I couldn't even make out what he was rabbiting on about as I drifted off to sleep.

I woke up this time on a beach surrounded by water. There was no sun and the sky was dark instead of blue. The sudden gust of wind brought the cold and made me aware that I was completely naked.

'Shit, it looks like a storm! A real bad one an' all!' The water began to sway violently, rising and splashing against the sand. That's where she came from. From the water, just like a mermaid.

'Susan, I'm over here!' my voice shouted. I knew it was McPherson's sister straightaway but what was she doing here, in my dream? She'd noticed me and had begun to smile. I was starting to shake with cold. It must have been some forgotten island near the North Pole, perhaps the start of a bad nightmare. I wanted the sun to come out and big Zelda again.

Suddenly, I was struck by a large stone that descended from the sky. It was covered in ice and was followed by even larger stones. Susan began to run towards the only tree on the island and I instantly followed her. Although she'd got a head start, I beat her to it and dived for the cover of its large rubbery leaves. She landed right on top of me. She was laughing. Her face touched mine and I felt her warmth like the sun's rays in my other dream. This time she was playing the game. Her face warming my chest as it made its way towards my navel. I began to breathe strangely. A different pattern. Sharp ... sharp ... gasp, that felt so nice.

I felt it coming this time and was determined to wake before I exploded, as I had done last time. The heat had finished playing and began to move closer and closer. Again I felt hard. This time really hard. The lightning lit up the dark sky around us. Susan let out a shrill shriek to coincide with the loud clap of thunder, that rolled nowhere, except over us. I had to shake myself awake. This didn't feel right anymore, not with McPherson in the tent.

Doing it with You is Taboo

It was the teeth that caused me to wake up. I felt the teeth. She was about to sink them into me. I grabbed hold of a handful of hair just as my eyes opened. It was dark. I'd returned to a place I knew. The orange cotton walls of the tent, were still there. To my surprise, then shock that turned into horror, I'd managed to bring the handful of hair back with me, back from my dream. That's when I felt the movement. Movement between my legs. The hair was straining to free itself from my grip. My imagination went wild as to what kind of creature had got inside the tent. I was on the verge of screaming, when the voice I recognised spoke.

I didn't talk to Girlie Boy McPherson all the way home from Anglesey. Everyone knew something was wrong between us but not what had taken place. I was confused and angry. McPherson had cheated me out of my dream but because I felt sorry for him, I intended to keep it to myself, for now. Apart from which, I didn't know how to go about telling anyone what he'd done.

'So, he's a poofter then?'

'I dunno!'

'He likes doing that then. Will he do me?'

'Yer Dad will do that for yer!'

'What?'

I told Jonesy that it was Danny Hawksley who had the problem. That way I knew he'd say nothing. He knew Danny would beat him up and his dad. Well he'd try anyway, Danny was off his head like that. I would deny ever telling him such a story. So Jonesy would have to listen and hopefully advise me. He had never been in that kind of situation before and found it a source of amusement. I laughed along with him in the end. I knew the whole subject freaked him out but he was my friend, so he listened. As I walked home, I thought about my mate's attitude and decided I was right not to tell anyone about Girlie Boy. He would be put under such stress and he didn't deserve that. I never told Jonesy that I'd exploded and how nice it all felt until I realised it wasn't a dream.

The front door of 521 loomed in front of me. My mind was miles away. I spoke to McPherson that evening for the first time since we returned two weeks ago. I could see he was pleased. I had said some nasty things to him that morning in the tent. Hurtful things. When I realised what it was he was doing I began to curse. I turned on the torch and he was looking up at me. His face unsure of how I was going to react.

'You freak. Get away from me you fucking dog.' He tried to speak but I told him I was going to beat him up. He sat on his sleeping bag and tears began to appear. I told him to get out of the tent before I set on him. I wanted to hurt him. He grabbed his towel and coat and quickly left. I lay there feeling angry but my feelings of anger were confused. I'd felt so nice. So warm. Why had he done that to me? I'd made up my mind to ask him, that night.

I had to wait until bedtime until I knew everyone was asleep. I had to pass through the McPhersons' bedroom to reach my own. It was nearly twelve thirty by my Mickey Mouse watch. I was going to wake Girlie Boy and have a good talk to him in the bathroom. It was safer there and I could also light up a smoke. I needed one. Girlie Boy appeared at the door half asleep.

'Shh! Close the door and lock it! Okay, just tell me why you did that, just tell me?' His face began to flush. I had to back off, I was coming on too strong.

'Cos.'

'Cos what?'

'Cos I like you, Rob, I thought you'd...'

'What!' I began to raise my voice and had to check myself. Girlie Boy began to frown.

'John, listen, I know sometimes I call yer Girlie Boy but you're not really a girl. Girls do that!' I could see he was thinking about what I'd said before he spoke.

'B-but Davy Green isn't a girl'

'What?'

'I said Davy Green...' I told him to shut up. We were changing venue.

'Come on, let's go to my room', I suggested, unlocking the door.

Davy Green, what's he been doing? My mind was firing questions as I led the way towards my bedroom. That's when I found out that Davy Green had been doing the same thing to McPherson. I told him I didn't think it was right. He said it felt so nice. I agreed. He then went on to tell me about his foster parents. The ones they'd been with, before they escaped and came to live with us. They used to lock him and his brothers inside a wardrobe while they went out. Susan would always have to go out with them wherever they went. I was listening to what he was saying, but my main thoughts were on Davy Green. How come I didn't know what was going on? I should have guessed. I asked Girlie Boy if Markie knew. I was kind of relieved he didn't. This meant he wasn't party to any of it. I was sure in my mind that I was going to tell Dotty Crystal in the morning. It must have been nearly morning already. I made a pact with McPherson before he went. We wouldn't say anything to anyone for now. I needed time to think about what effect it was going to have when I did tell.

I watched McPherson all week. I'd catch him in some kind of trance. The problem was, he kept staring at me at the tea table and he was beginning to get on my nerves. I was fifteen, McPherson was fourteen. I was black he was white. He had a problem and the more I tried to carry it, the more I got involved. I began to notice how happy he was to do things for me and the way he was always smiling at me. 'He wants to be your friend,' Gwen had said to me. 'He looks up to you Rob...' But I knew his problem and it was beginning to confuse me.

He came to my bedroom two weeks later. It was well after twelve o'clock. I'd been spending most of my time at Jonesy's house and purposely avoiding McPherson. He didn't knock but I moved when I sensed the door was open. The 'pretend to be asleep' ploy wasn't going to work.

'Rob, are you awake?'

'I am now, Johnny, what d'yer want?' I replied, trying to stay civil. Then I noticed he was crying.

'Nightmares, I'm having nightmares. Can I sit with you a for a bit?'

'I dunno, if Dotty comes...'

'She won't, Rob, she won't.' He was already sitting himself at the edge of my bed. I sat up and looked at him. His eyes looked blotchy and wet. For some reason he had tied his hair into a pony tail. He really looked like his sister now.

'John, sit on the chair!', I suggested.

'Why?'

'Cos that's why!' His eyes began to narrow at my evasion.

'It's cold by the window!' he argued. I just laughed and he quickly joined in.

I was glad he'd gone by the time Dotty did her morning roll check. The last thing I remember was hearing the voice of Girlie Boy. He must have been there all night. I thought about my dreams in the tent, about his sister Susan and how much he looked like her. Did I fancy him? I certainly liked her. He was forcing me to like him as well. I was confused and began to cry. He asked me what was wrong. I couldn't tell him I was scared. Scared of him. For some reason, he also began to cry. We didn't talk. The comfort of holding each other was enough. Other intentions just weren't there. His heartbeat was pounding on my chest. I listened to the rhythm. It sounded out of tune. I lay there with him until I woke up. It was half past six and I was glad he'd returned to his own bed.

It didn't mean anything to me then but, if we'd been caught, it would have been a major issue. The following week we broke up for the Whit holiday. No school for a whole week. Davy Green was home but the vibes around the house had gone stale. Girlie Boy kept trying to demonstrate that he was some good friend of mine. It was all a game to wind up Davy and, sure enough, me and Greeny clashed.

Danny Hawksley left 521 soon after big Zelda. Shy Katy was going back to Greece to live with her father. Rumours were afloat that the home was closing down. I didn't believe it.

The sudden good news that they'd found my mother living in Sheffield was a turning point in my life. I was so excited when the social workers told me that we'd shortly be going to visit her and my two sisters. It all happened sooner than I had expected. Just one week later we were driving across the Snake Pass and across the Derbyshire moors. I felt really strange meeting her at first. As we entered the huge estate, containing high-rise blocks and yet more high-rise blocks, I began to get butterflies in my stomach. I ended up staying for a whole week. In the end though, I couldn't wait to get away. Maybe I was too old to be held and loved. I think our reunion had been left too late. I was nearly sixteen and the woman who had given birth to me was a complete stranger.

I don't know whether she sensed my discontent. I hated church and my mother insisted that all her children went every Sunday while she lay in bed with her latest fling. In the first week, I saw her lose her temper and hit my younger sister with a broomstick. I was soon informed that I had a different father from my two sisters. So that meant we were only half brother and sisters, or something like that. I couldn't understand. The cruel effect of this knowledge was enough; enough to drive me away from what I'd been pining for all my life. I had met my mother and knew there and then that there was something missing. I didn't find out what it was until I returned eight years later.

Back at 521, things were really boring. The arrival of a new boy didn't liven the place up. 'Why did people have to leave?' I asked myself. I was missing Danny and Big Zelda, Katy and Davy. I always wished Markie would come back and be with me but it never happened. I hated myself and I hated my life. I opened the curtains and sat on the chair. I could see the whole sky, sparkling with stars. My bedroom window was one of the biggest in the house. I could see the ugly minibus in the driveway below. It must have been nearly twelve. I was pissed off, lonely and about to climb into bed. I'd stopped wearing pyjamas in favour of footy shorts and a vest. I'd seen the geezer in my mother's house sleeping like that. She liked him a lot. I knew that because he received far more attention from her than I did. The tears just seemed to appear on my cheeks. I started to breathe heavily, a sure sign that I wanted to bawl out loud, scream and smash things up. I didn't hear Girlie Boy enter the room. He was standing right beside me before I noticed him.

'Why are you crying again? Don't say yer not!'

'Yes I am, I hate this fucking place, that's why!' I lied. I couldn't tell him the real reason for my distress. I felt his hand touch my shoulder.

'Sit down, Rob. Sit down', he suggested in his concerned voice.

'I'll be okay, Johnny, I'll be okay,' I told him, as he sat down beside me on my bed. He had that look in his eye. I knew what his intentions were. That's when I noted he'd discarded the pyjamas he had been wearing earlier. He only had his vest and underpants on. I looked at his white skin, his shapeless legs. I looked at him. He had been watching me. He smiled and placed his hand on my leg.

'No, Johnny, no, I can't!'

'Why?'

'Cos that makes us queers. You know, poofs. That means we can't have babies. I don't want to be a queer.'

'You want my sister, then?'

'No, I don't, she'll tell everyone!'

'Don't you get lonely then? I do.' I had to think about how to answer this question. I'd always been lonely.

'Yes, I do get lonely,' I admitted.

'So do I, a real lot.' I began to climb into the bed and cover myself in the blankets. Johnny was still watching my every move.

'It's taboo, taboo!' I hissed at him, turning to face the wall. 'Go to bed, Johnny!'

I lay there for some time. I knew he hadn't gone. He was still there sitting in my chair. I was sure he'd stay there all night. I turned around only to to see that the fool was still smiling. I sighed. He knew he'd won.

End of an Era

The playroom was empty. Most of the toys had gone, along with the McPhersons. They were the last to leave, except for me of course. Maybe I should have been happy with the whole house to myself. I had a cook, a cleaner and two minders. Aunty Gwen and Julie rotated shifts to look after me. I'd already been told that the search for somewhere for me to live was going on in earnest. They had asked if I wanted to go back to my mother's. I declined the offer. I didn't think she liked me. She lived in a council house that was barely carpeted. Money was scarce and I was used to plenty of spending money and not having to clean up after myself.

I was upset that 521 had to close down. We all cried on the day we were informed by Dotty. The two young McPhersons started first and they were quickly joined by their sister Susan. I tried to keep my emotions hidden but surrounded by a room of watery eyes, I gave way. No matter how upset we were, they had decided that closing the home was the answer. Who were we to say any different? I couldn't say anything and neither could Johnny Mac. We both knew one of the reasons things had come to this. I'd been told I should have known better and shouldn't have allowed things to go so far, or as far as they thought things had gone. But just what did they know? I was very angry at first. Angry at him for not leaving my room before roll check but I was also hurt by the way the adults regarded the situation. Despite the fact that they'd been told that this behaviour had been going on inside the home for over four years, they regarded the present situation as a good enough reason to close 521.

Placing a Desmond Decker record on the turntable, I began to think about Markie. 'The Israelites' was booming from the speaker. I began to think about the folks I'd met recently, Mr. and Mrs. Carmichael. I didn't like them, he was a priest who ran a small church in Belvidere Road. They lived in a large house off High Park Street, a poor and run down area in Liverpool 8. I didn't want to leave the pleasant suburb of Aigburth and the thought of living under the rules of a white Jesus worshipper scared me. I was black, so he wasn't my Jesus, he was theirs. Every time I looked at the shiny white dog collar, my ancestors walked over my spine.

'No, Aunty, I really don't like them!'

'Why? You've only just met them, you haven't given them much of a chance.'

'Can't I just stay here?'

'You know that's not possible, we've spoken about this before.'

Yes we had and Gwen had explained that they couldn't afford to run a large house just for one child. I knew I'd have to go somewhere soon. My social worker was returning again the next day. I think he was pissed off that I hadn't gladly gone to the Carmichael's but my instincts had told me to say no. I was being taken to a hostel. Maybe to shock me. I don't know what I was expecting but when I arrived, I wished I'd taken the first option. But it was too late.

Most of my things were packed for me. It was raining as I took my last walk around the garden. The den had been neglected and was falling down already. I went inside and took my last look at the dining room. For a second I almost thought I saw Markie sitting at the table, eating scrambled eggs. The rain was splashing against the window sill outside. My social worker had arrived but I was determined to make him wait. Wait until I was ready. My eyes were burning as I fought back my tears. I swore I'd never cry again after that day.

I was to be the last child to leave 521 Aigburth Road. I looked back at Gwen and Julie, as they waved me off down the driveway. I sighed. My social worker was cold and had a job to do. He had to get me to 5 Fern Grove, Toxteth, Liverpool 8. I was on my way to Ujamma House, a hostel for homeless black teenagers. What that meant was beyond me. I was also in for a rude awakening. I was scared out of my wits. This was a new adventure. One I had to make on my own. I felt abandoned and totally alone.

Why?

Fern Grove, Liverpool 8, was situated at the bottom of Lodge Lane; a busy street, full of shops including a post office, banks, bakeries, hardware stores and a cash and carry. There was a swimming bath and a bingo hall at the top. It was also a major bus route and had its fair share of public houses, the closest to us being the Croxteth Arms. Fern Grove itself, ran to the bottom of Hartington Road but wasn't accessible to vehicle traffic. Opposite a hole-in-the-wall garage were two three-storey buildings. We had stopped outside number five. Ujamma House was a hostel set up for homeless black teenagers by Merseyside Community Relations Council, whose main office was situated in the city centre. I was suffering from stomach cramps, as my social worker drew up outside the yellow front gate.

'Yep!' That was the first word the man had spoken since leaving 521.

We were greeted at the door by a small white woman, wearing glasses. She introduced herself as Pauline. Leading the way, she took us into a narrow passage towards a steep set of stairs. At the foot of these, I noticed a front door to what looked like a ground floor apartment. As I reached the bottom of the first flight, the door opened and a young girl appeared. I was to learn that she was, in fact, much older than me.

Following Pauline up the stairs, behind my social worker, we finally reached the first landing. I could see the stairs continuing upwards. We entered a door into another passage with four doors. The one at the far end was the residents' living room, the middle one was the staff office and, at the other end, was a bedroom and a bathroom. We had entered the office.

After going through all the introductions and paper work, I was taken upstairs to the top of the house where the kitchen was! It was the first time I'd seen such a scruffy-looking kitchen. Behind the other three doors were a bathroom, next to a small bedroom and, at the end of the corridor, a large bedroom. My heart sank when I saw that it contained three beds, two of them made up already. I wasn't too keen on the idea of sharing again. The bed I had been given was beside the only window. Above me in the corner, was the attic trap door. The window looked down onto the garage and the street below.

Before I'd pushed my suitcase and bags out of sight under my new bed, my social worker entered. He informed me he was leaving. He forgot to ask me if I was okay but that's how it was. I was on my own. Pauline came up, bringing with her a strange-looking blanket and a green sheet.

'This is a quilt, I'll bring you a cover later, would you like two pillows or one?'

'Two please, Aunty,' I replied.

'Oh … and you don't have to call me Aunty you know, just plain Pauline will do,' she explained with a smile. I returned her smile with one of my own. I asked her who else slept in the room and she informed me that they were Tommy Williams and Ray Cooder who were both at school. Ray was also a new boy and had only arrived the day before.

'They're both nice lads,' she told me as she turned to leave the room. 'I'll bring those other things up later. You can come and watch telly downstairs when you're ready.' I liked her immediately. As I looked at the other two beds in the room, I thought about what my new room mates would be like. It was about half past three and I reckoned I'd just be leaving the art room if I'd been at school. I was missing 521 already.

I still hadn't met the warden in charge. I'd been told he was due in shortly and that he lived on the premises with his family. They were situated on the ground floor. The woman who'd appeared at the door at the foot of the stairs was the warden's wife, Margaret. She came up to say hello. Again, I thought how young she looked. She was very attractive too, her smile almost like Aunty Gwen's. I tried hard to disguise the horror on my face when her husband returned. When he entered the house, the stench of fear came with him.

Playing the Game

I met Tommy Williams first. He was a small Ugandan lad and although he was the same age as me, he had the physique of a twelve year old. His complexion was darker than mine. He introduced himself before disappearing downstairs. I didn't want to go down there yet but I knew I'd have to soon. Everyone must have been home by now. I could hear quite a lot of activity coming from the floors below.

My thoughts had turned to school. I was sixteen and in my final year. I knew I'd flunked my mock exams and was aware that the real exams were due any time now. I wasn't going to be prepared for them, I hadn't even been studying. School had become a joke, a place to let off steam and meet my mates from under the bridge. Garston Bridge was where I now hung out since I'd fallen out with my best mate Jonesy. I think he was receiving too much peer pressure for hanging around with me. I was now a member of the Wimpey Boot Boys. They hung around Window Lane and I was the only coloured boy in the gang. Sporting my Dr. Martens and half-mast jeans, I'd become a skinhead.

The sudden entrance of Raymond Cooder brought me back to the present. He was the complete opposite of Tommy. Although he was black, I could see by his attire, that he was different. He had a weird hair style. His tightly-knit black Afro was wedge-shaped. I also noticed his black, pointed shoes and black PVC pants which looked ready to burst. He was also watching me but no words passed between us. After giving me a final glance, he left the room. My stomach began to roll over. It must be teatime.

I remembered chasing a boy who wore pointed shoes, like my new room mate. I'd been with the Boot Boys when we noticed the punk rocker. They were our enemies but I'd never seen a black punk before, if that was what Ray Cooder was.

Pauline returned, bringing with her two pillows and a quilt cover.

'You'd best come and meet Mr. Sunny, he's waiting in the

office.' I already knew that he was the man in charge. I immediately thought of Frank Purdy when I saw Stanley Sunny. Not only was he larger than Fat Frank but he was also black. This was the first time I'd seen a really fat black person.

'My name's Stan, Stanley Sunny and I'm in charge here,' he informed me, quite politely.

'I'm Robbie Suilerman,' I replied, offering my hand.

'Yes, yes!' He began to shake his large head. His excessive face flab began to wobble from his cheeks down to his double chins. His large hand enveloped mine as he began to squeeze. Then, just as quickly as he'd tightened it, he loosened his grip. I figured this was meant to be some kind of friendly gesture. I was still amazed at the sheer size of the guy. His stomach was clearly visible and hanging over the belt of his jeans. As he turned to lean over the desk, I resisted the urge to laugh at the sight of his large brown bottom. I realised that it wasn't that his pants were falling down, he was just too fat for the jeans and the scruffy shirt he was trying to wear.

'Now, this is a copy of the rules we have here,' he told me, handing me a typed piece of paper. I read the first line, which said that residents must share in the cooking and cleaning.

'Okay, you can go now, go and have your tea upstairs in the kitchen.' I scrambled out of the small office escaping the strong, overpowering stench of body odour. Frank Purdy used to smell sweaty all the time too.

I was fascinated by the thought of being around people of the same colour as me. My two new room mates were black, as was Desramona Browne, the tall, thin girl I'd seen in the kitchen on my way downstairs. Dessi was originally from Manchester. If it hadn't been for the large gap in her front teeth and her wafer-thin figure, she would have been very attractive.

The residents' sitting room was down the hallway from the office. It contained a television set which was the only decent object in there. The furniture looked in a bad way. The large, green sofa had collapsed; its material stained and ripped, the cushions saggy and worn. Ray Cooder sat on one of the armchairs in front of the gas fire, engrossed in the television programme. I allowed the door to close and made my way back upstairs towards the kitchen. Desramona and Tommy were cooking and the kitchen was in chaos. There was a deep frying pan on top of the large gas cooker and the noise of the potatoes in the hot fat could be heard from the bottom of the stairs. The smell wasn't too healthy either but, by now, I was starving. Chicken pies appeared from the mouth of the oven and some baked beans sat in a greasy-looking pan on the wooden dining table.

'Hiya!' It was Desramona who first noticed me standing by the door. 'Come on, come in, you're sitting over there.' She nodded towards a set place in the far corner. As Tommy began to dish out the beans, I counted seven plates and I'd only met three people so far.

'Dinner's ready!' shouted Dessi towards the stairs. 'I mean tea,' she half muttered to herself. Footsteps began to charge up the stairs. Ray Cooder was the first to enter. He was followed by a white girl, Cathy Silk. The first thing I noticed about Cathy, was that her large nose matched her large chest. She had long, dark-brown hair that looked well cared for.

The chips looked cooked, well-cooked. I just hoped that Tom had the decency to remove all the black bits before serving them out. He didn't. I received a plate full of crisps, beans and a chicken pie.

For a big man he moved quietly, none of us heard him coming up the stairs. His sudden appearance at the kitchen door changed the atmosphere. The smell of food was soon over-powered by body odour. The huge man's frame had blocked out the passage outside the kitchen. He just stood there shaking his head. Desramona began to laugh.

'Hey, Stan, you gonna watch us eat then?' she asked, still grinning.

'You shut it!' came his light-hearted reply. 'Tom, you empty the bins after you've finished.'

'Okay, Stan,' replied little Tom. That's when I picked up on the vibe. I wasn't sure what it was yet, but Tom had gone sheepish.

'Is everything okay, Robert?' he asked, nodding in my direction.

'Yes Sir,' I replied. This set them all off into fits of laughter, except Stan.

'Hey! don't be laughing at him, you lot. I like that. You call me sir!' This brought more peals of laughter from the others around the table.

'He's only winding yer up,' said Desramona smiling at me.

I noticed that the only people who were not really amused by it all were Tom and me. He began to clear his plates from the table. Stan soon returned downstairs. His descent was heard loud and clear. I began to suspect that he had sneaked up on us that first time. For such a large man, he had moved very quietly. I also made a note of little Tom's reluctance to join in the banter with the warden, Stanley Sunny.

Exams

My return to school the following day was the beginning of my truancy. I had CSE exams at the end of the month. I was so tired as I sat upstairs on the 86 bus. I'd had to walk to the top of Lodge Lane to catch it on Smithdown Road. My journey took ages and I had missed my stop. Already late, I would have to run up a large hill to reach the school gate. I decided to walk. On reaching the gate, I caught sight of Yozzer, trying to hide behind a large pillar beside the main doors. I wondered whether he would ever change that worn grey pinstripe suit. Yozzer, Mr. Hughes, was my form tutor. Everyone called him Yozzer or Popeye and a number of other names but always 'Sir' to his face. I could pretend I'd been to the lower school in Heath Road but he'd ask why and, whatever excuse I used, he'd check up on it. He had probably watched me strolling up the hill. I was in trouble. That was nothing new. Yozzer and me met at least twice a week. I'd been caned three times, in my first and second years. The last time it happened, I ended up throwing a book after the teacher who did it because he didn't have the authority to cane me in the first place.

'Well, what time do you call this, young man?'

'Sorry Sir, b-but I have to travel further to get here now!'

'Yes, we are aware of your situation, that's why today you won't be disciplined but you know the route now, so on time in the morning. Off you go!'

'Yes Sir, thanks.'

'Shit head!' I whispered, as I sprinted up the stairs towards the classroom.

It was maths with Betty Carmichael. We called her 'Granny'. She was old, which meant that the maths lessons were a waste of time, as she couldn't control our class. We were class Five D. There were A, B, C and we were D, the dregs of the fifth year. We'd all been assessed throughout our attendance at New Heys. I began in class One B but by the second year I'd been demoted to class Two C. Now, in my last year, I'd made it to the bottom of the heap. Class Five D; the no hopers, the rowdies, who every teacher tried to avoid. That's why we had maths with Granny Carmichael and not Ms. Pipper.

I decided to stop at the window of the class next door; geography with Mr. Davis. It was my old mate Jonesy's class – class Five A. He had elevated himself and I hated him for not being my mate any more. His head was in his books as usual. I made a mental promise to give him some stick if I saw him later when I was with my mates. I found myself getting on his brief regularly, enticing others to set on him but I would often intervene if he was getting hurt. I just wanted him to be my friend again. I was no longer up to the grade I suppose.

As always, the maths lesson was spent throwing paper planes and making jokes. The sound of the breaktime bell started the rowdy movement out onto the playing fields.

'Hey Robbo! You coming the shops?'

'Who you callin' Robbo, knob head?'

It was Charlie Edwards. I was hanging round with him. He lived in Belle Vale and caught the same bus home as me.

He knew I hated being called Robbo so, of course, that was what he called me to wind me up. We had PE next lesson and that was okay since I enjoyed playing football. Charlie and me had entered for the school team but we were from 4D and didn't get picked. My mate Jonesy did. In fact, he became the star player and I hated him even more for that.

Dinner time was spent at the local shops. Charlie had decided he was going home after dinner.

'But what if Yozzer finds out?'

'He won't, I always go home in the afternoons!'

'How do yer get marked in lessons then?'

'I don't, are you coming?'

'Na, I'd best not!'

'Come on, let's go to town, I can see me mate, he works in the market.' I was soon travelling towards the city centre on the same bus that had taken me to school a couple of hours earlier. This was the first time I'd played truant and I was a bit nervous. Charlie was in his element.

We got off the bus outside Lewis's on Ranelagh Street. Charlie was moving quickly, darting in and out between shoppers. We'd crossed a main road beside H. Samuels, a large jewellers.

'Me old man's going to have that one off!' Charlie informed me.

'What?'

'That jeweller's shop. Him and his mates, honest!' I just laughed because I knew when he was telling lies. Charlie was always making things up – his dad also took part in the Great Train Robbery and all that.

Reaching the sliding doors to St. John's Precinct was a relief. Charlie said we'd be safe in there. Inside the crowded market, the strong smell of the fish and fruit hit us. Charlie darted off again, this time towards some escalators.

'Wait for me then!' but Charlie was already at the top heading towards his mate, Tago, who looked younger than us.

I had caught sight of a gang of black lads standing beside a cafe, with a few white girls amongst them. They seemed to be having a good time.

'Hey Charlie, I'm going over here!' I called out, as I

moved towards the group I'd been watching. I expected him to follow but, before I realised he hadn't, I was already there. They all stopped talking and looked at me. That's when I noticed I'd lost Charlie. All the lads had big Afros and were carrying picks. It was the one with the biggest Afro that spoke.

'Hey, nigger, what the fuck you want here, hey?'

'Yeah, you're too dark, man, too dark, move on!' The second lad had a similar complexion to Markie's, light brown. The third lad was even lighter. I was the darkest and began to feel as though I'd made a mistake when an arm reached around my neck, pulling me to the floor.

'Hey, hey!' I was about to panic, when I recognised the pants and trainers. It was Tom Williams from the hostel.

'So you're sagging, are yer?'

'And you?'

'Yeah, I always come here. I was going to say this morning, but...'

'But what?'

'You coming tomorrow then? Come 'ead, let's get off from here, Robbie. Them lot are dick heads.'

'Where you going 'cos I'm with me mate from school?'

'Who?'

'Some boy, his name's Charlie.'

'A white boy, Robbie?'

'Yeah.'

'Come on, let's go. Leave him here!'

'But-but!' That's as far as I got. Tom was moving off towards the stairs and the exit. I couldn't see Charlie anywhere.

'Wait for me then, mate!'

Tom explained to me how he'd been in town all day. He often played truant from Arundel Comprehensive, his school on Lodge Lane.

'Listen, Robbie. I'll let yer in on something but don't tell no-one, okay?'

'Yeah!'

'Tomorrow we're going to make some money, you and me.'

'Doing what, Tom?'

'You'll find out if yer come.' I knew I'd go because I'd started to hate school and Tom seemed like a good lad.

'Yeah, I'll come with yer tomorrow, mate.'

It was when we arrived back at 5 Fern Grove, that I discovered why Tommy went really timid when Stanley Sunny was around. He was waiting at the front door. 'Hi!' I said and he moved to let me pass but he did not allow my new mate Tom through, as he'd allowed me to do. I didn't see the punch but the sound from Tom made me turn and look. Tom had dropped to his knees, all the wind knocked out off him.

'So, what have you been up to, hey?' By now, I was standing halfway up the staircase. Stanley had a tight grip on Tom, who began to wriggle in order to escape. This seemed to make matters worse for him. Stanley began to stand on his legs, making full use of his large body weight by pushing his hands against the walls. Tom began to scream. That's when I turned and fled upstairs. I was shaking as I reached the bathroom. I sat on the toilet and held my head in my hands. I could still hear Tom screaming. I couldn't believe it. Not again. Not another one.

The Joker and the Bully

The school bell rang and the rush for the gates was on. Great! We had the whole weekend ahead of us. The exams were due to start on the following Monday. Everyone was ready for them, except class 5 D. Many of us had been truanting during the year and I had no real idea how well or badly I would do but I'd never know unless I tried.

The bus stop was crowded as usual and an old lady began to protest as the bus arrived. Nobody listened to her complaints. She'd have to wait until we'd all boarded. There was no respect in those days. Charlie was sitting at the front of the bus and I took my usual seat at the back. An inspector had got on and was checking tickets. I had a bus pass but I knew that Charlie's pass was a forgery. He had to flash it in front of the driver to board but it would never pass close scrutiny. The inspector had come upstairs and started to walk towards the back. I already had my pass out for inspection. After taking a long look at it, he returned it to me. The bus began to draw to a halt and I could see a large crowd from Quarry Bank School, waiting to board. Charlie had to make his move fast and get off the bus. He just made it as the inspector was moving in on him. Opening the sliding window, I called after him.

'You got no money, lad?'

'No.'

I knew Charlie had a long way to walk. I had fifty pence, my last fifty pence but I was getting dole money this week. Even though I hadn't left school yet, the hostel had sorted that out. I began to wave to Charlie as the bus moved off, he looked pretty miserable. I caught his surprise and delight as I flung the fifty pence piece at him. He began to wave as I disappeared from his view. I'll get that back tomorrow I thought to myself. Anyway, I had more serious problems to face; how to deal with a bully.

I arrived back at Fern Grove at around five past four. Desramona was the only other resident at home. Having changed out of my crumpled school uniform, I decided to go and have a chat with Pauline. She was on duty today, which meant she'd be here until the next morning since all the staff worked twenty-four hour shifts. She was in the office.

'Hi Aunty, sorry I mean Pauline ... I keep forgetting!'

'Okay,' she smiled, 'how was school today?'

'Alright.'

'Good.'

I wished she was in overall charge but she was only the deputy to Stanley Sunny. He worried me. I'd been here for two weeks and I'd started to see things that I didn't like at all. Pauline told me that Vinny would be on duty tomorrow. I'd met Vinny Graham on my second day. He was West Indian and looked like he could handle himself yet I was quick to note that even he was wary around Stan Sunny. In fact everyone was, except Ray Cooder.

Ray was the first black punk I'd ever come across and I think I was probably the first black skinhead he'd seen. We couldn't have been more opposite in the way we dressed. I had figured out a way to deal with our bully. So had Ray, but I knew from the first time he tried his ploy that he had got it all wrong.

Stanley Sunny had two sons and two Alsatian dogs with a litter of pups that lived in the back yard. His two sons lived with him and his young wife Margaret on the ground floor. Stephen Sunny, who was three years old, was built like a miniature Sumo wrestler. 'Like father like son,' I thought, the first time I met him at the residents' house meeting. These were held in Stanley's front room. It must have been Ray Cooder's first meeting too because this is where he made himself an enemy of Stan Sunny.

Ray the punk, was a natural-born joker. Unfortunately, his idea of a good joke was usually at other people's expense. If someone had a visible mole, a long nose or a twitch, Ray Cooder was going to confront them about it. True to form, at the first meeting he and I attended, he felt perfectly justified in telling Stanley Sunny – and everyone else in the room – that his son was much too overweight. This might not have been so bad as he had meant it to be funny, but he then pushed it too far by grabbing hold of Stephen, to demonstrate how heavy he was! I only had to observe everyone's face in the room to know that Cooder had over-stepped the mark. He was the only one laughing and it didn't take him long to suss out he'd put his foot in it. I'll give him that.

The meeting was brought to a sudden close and we were all ushered back upstairs to the residents' quarters; the lounge with the green sofa. I went straight upstairs to our room. Tom soon joined me.

'Shit! Did you hear Ray? Ha-ha-ha. Stan will get him back for that!'

'What d'yer mean, Tom?'

'You watch, Stan didn't like that.'

'Shh! He might hear yer, you know he creeps about!'

'Fat bastard, isn't he, Rob? Just a fat bastard!'

'Say it to his face then, Tom.'

'You mad? I know, ask Cooder to do it for a joke!'

'Yeah, he'd do it as well!'

'Come on, let's go and watch telly.'

'I'll be down in a bit, Tom.'

I liked Tommy Williams. He was lively and I'd promised to play truant with him next week. He said he had a mission, whatever that meant. I was soon to find out. It was after one o'clock before we went to bed and, even then, we didn't stop talking until after three. We were woken up with a bang at seven o'clock.

'Come on, you lot, get up. This whole place needs cleaning from top to bottom. Move, come on!' It was him, the fat bastard. Storming towards my bed, which was beside the window, he flung the blinds open.

'Tom, come on, move it!' he began to shout now 'and you, Cooder … NOW!'

My feet were already on the carpet. So were Tom's. On seeing that Ray had sat up, Stanley began to give us his commands.

'Right, you can start in here. Then Tom, you and Rob do the kitchen, I want it spotless. Cooder, you can start washing the bins and rest rooms, okay? Get a move on!' With that said, he stormed out of the room. Tom shrugged his shoulders and sighed. Ray lay back down and turned to face the wall. I was about to speak but Tom signalled to me to remain silent, just as the door swung open again. He must have been standing outside the door.

'Cooder, get your fucking arse out that bed!' Ray shot bolt upright, as if not yet realising where he was or who was talking to him.

'Feet on the floor, Cooder, right now!' came Sunny's final command. He moved from the doorway to take up a position close to Cooder's bed. Ray had placed his feet on the floor but Stanley still stood over him. Ray began to smile. I could sense one of his jokes coming on but this just wasn't the time for one. I looked at Tom who was beginning to cringe. Stanley had his back to me and he was beginning to breathe heavily. I caught Cooder's attention and began to shake my head in the hope that he'd get the message. One wrong move, and the large man was bound to punch him.

'I'm first in the bathroom!' I announced, standing up and moving towards the door.

'Stan, there's no toilet roll,' I informed him as I opened the door. He was still glaring at Ray. Tom continued shrugging his shoulders.

'I'll use last night's Echo then, fuck it!'

Tom sniggered but my attempts to break the tension weren't working.

Shop Lifting

I really wanted to look at the girl's paper beside me but that was cheating. The teacher at the front of the hall was watching for cheats. I might as well not have been there, it was the maths exam and I was utterly useless at maths. Adding up wasn't a problem, neither was taking things away, but when it got to algebra and multiplication, I was lost.

I could see Charlie over at the other side of the hall. He seemed to be asleep, which was just what I felt like doing too. I soon began day-dreaming, thinking how lucky Ray Cooder was the other day. He apologised to Stan and then went on to make us laugh with a string of jokes about fat people. Of course, this was after Stanley had gone downstairs. However, Vinny was about. I wasn't surprised that he found Ray Cooder's comments funny, I don't think he really liked our warden. Maybe I could work on that. I had to find out where his loyalties lay. Something had to be done about the fat man, he seemed to be getting worse. It was Tom that I felt sorry for, he always seemed to be on the receiving end; Sunny's personal punch bag, always there for when he felt frustrated.

I began to suss out why he always singled out Tom and not Ray Cooder or myself. It was obvious that Ray didn't think; he would just say the first thing that came into his head to amuse people. He also had family who lived quite near so Stan had to be careful. In my case, the fact that I still received visits from my social worker from Dr. Barnado's probably made him think twice before striking out at me. Although Tom had a social worker too – a black woman who he was in love with – she had gone to school with Stanley and so was no good for his cause.

The sound of the whistle ending the two hour exam couldn't have come sooner and I headed for the bus to town to have my lunch. Although I had a geography exam scheduled for the afternoon, I'd promised to meet Tom as he had a plan to make some money and I wasn't going to miss out. We met up inside St. John's Market. Tom was with a few other lads but left them as I approached.

'Who are they, Tom?'

'Lads from the area. The one with the Afro is Jimmy Pie, he's got a brother called Johnny. He's in the nick, though!'

'You been to jail then, Tom?'

'Na, I've been nicked though. I stole a handbag from some office. Got caught and fined and sent to the hostel!'

'Where we going, Tom?'

'Army and Navy, and when we get in there just watch me, okay?'

The British Army and Navy Stores was next to H. Samuel's and opposite Lewis's. Downstairs, the shopfloor contained rows of jackets and coats. Further on inside, were boots, hats and gloves. The menswear and camping departments were upstairs and Tom had already pressed for the elevator. The lift was only big enough to hold three people at the most and we crammed in with a white guy and his girl. Our journey up was made in silence.

Tom had gone to try on a pair of pinstripe pants. I was being helped by the assistant. Although I didn't have a bean to spend, I knew I had to play along. Tom re-appeared, giving the pinstripe pants back to the man.

'Na, I don't like them. Mind if I look around?' he asked.

'No, carry on sir,' replied the shop assistant. Tom winked at me. I was still unsure why. The arrival of more shoppers sent the assistant off to help them.

'Pick a pair you like then,' suggested Tom, standing by

the row of pants in front of me.

I liked the denims, the beige ones. Tom returned to the changing rooms and the assistant had watched him enter. I began to think he was mad when he returned and handed the assistant the beige pants that I had asked for.

'Na, mate, they're crap, we're going to shop around. Come 'ead!' he said, nodding at me to follow. I was still wondering why we'd just gone through that routine. Tom kept walking as I tried to get his attention. Reaching the bottom of the stairs, he headed for the exit. 'Some money-making scheme,' I thought, as I trailed behind him onto the street and into the rush hour crowds.

'Got yer bus pass?'

'Yeah!'

'Come on, we'll get a bus home.'

'But Tom, what about..?'

'Never mind, here's the bus.' We caught the bus and soon arrived at Prince's Park.

It wasn't until we began our walk up Bentley Road and towards Lodge Lane, that Tom produced two pairs of brand new pants. I was dumb-founded, completely speechless, before whooping for joy.

'How the – how the fuck did you do that, Tom?' He was just laughing. I knew it would take me all night to get him to reveal his secret. He'd made me swear I'd tell no-one else. I promised I wouldn't and he promised to tell me how to do it. We could go back tomorrow if I wanted to but I'd have to learn to do some of the work, so that night he would teach me. No-one asked about school and I didn't volunteer any information. I was happy. Me and my new mate were about to earn a small fortune.

That night, Tom took me to a house on Kingsley Road. Inside sat a small, black man, with long, matted hair. Tom told me he was called Judah, that he was a Rastaman and that they all grew long hair and, according to Tom, they didn't even comb it. I laughed. It wasn't until we reached another house, that I sussed out Tom's reason for visiting the Rastaman. I had only ever smoked packs of ten Park Drive and had just graduated to Benson and Hedges. It was one of these that I saw Tom destroy before placing its tobacco in a large sheet of Rizla. After quickly rolling it into a large cigarette, he asked me for a light. The sweet smell of the tobacco began to blow in my direction and made me inquisitive. It wasn't long before I asked for a go. One pull was enough. I coughed and spluttered. Tom and the woman whose house we were in, laughed at me. Tom said it was sensemillia. I knew ganja was a drug and I began to wait for the after-effects. I asked if it could make you see things and if it could kill you. They said it was no worse than a cigarette but the question as to whether I'd become addicted or not went unanswered. I decided not to smoke it again.

It was the next Friday and the city centre was packed. We'd had to allow Ray Cooder to come with us because he'd sussed something was going on. I had to laugh at the large coat he'd decided to wear for the mission. We were going to hit two main stores, Owen Owens and the Army and Navy. Tom and me already had a large collection of stolen trousers, casually hanging up in our wardrobes as though we'd paid for them.

Entering Owen Owens, we made our way towards the menswear department. We had separated at this point as there were plenty of shop assistants about the store. Ray was already being approached by a young-looking feller in a pinstripe suit. I could see Tom rummaging through a large rack of jeans. I laughed to myself as we began the mission.

Returning to the Army and Navy Store we had handsfull of shopping inside plastic carrier bags. No-one was to know that we hadn't paid for any of it. Tom was really excited. Ray had managed to keep three shop assistants occupied with a string of his latest jokes, whilst Tom and I had helped ourselves and vanished, before he reached the punch line. I could imagine them laughing as Ray made his exit. We'd had a good day, with fifteen pairs of pants between us.

The next task was to get them into the hostel unnoticed. Tom knew Stan wouldn't allow stolen property in the place. We had to be careful. Anyway, that's why Ray had been wearing his silly-looking overcoat. He had no chance shop lifting in it, they would have been onto him right away. However, the staff at Ujamma were used to Ray and the overcoat by now. Having reached the top of Bentley Road, we began to give Ray the bags. They quickly disappeared inside the sleeves and secret pockets of the heavy, punk overcoat. Ray looked a bit bulky but he was game.

Tom suggested I should go in first and he would bring up the rear. I had to find a reason to talk to the fat man and keep him occupied while leaving the front door open. Ray would be in next. Even if Stanley saw Cooder, he wouldn't pay him much attention. It would be Tom he'd be waiting for. Tom had been successfully avoiding his beatings lately. Ray and me often had to side-track the bully. In fact, Ray had the knack of making him feel self-conscious just by being around him. I just used to batter him with questions, I knew his small mind would take time to answer.

I'd completed my part of the plan. I saw Ray entering through the front door. The fat man was still explaining to me why the local lads used to fight the skinheads. His wife was out with the kids, so he had time on his hands and that wasn't good.

'How's the dogs, Stan?' The conversation definitely needed changing from the skinhead topic.

'Hungry – hungry for flesh!' he replied whilst glaring at me.

'One of them's had pups again, hasn't it?' I asked, trying to keep him sensible.

'Even they're fucking hungry!'

'Well I'm off then, Stan. See yer later, mate!'

I was already close to the door, so making my exit from his apartment wasn't hard. Ray was already stashing our wares inside the airing cupboard. I'd just sat down on the bed when I realised Tom had yet to get into the house, not that getting in was his problem. The sudden, high-pitched yelp could have come from one of Fatso's dogs but it was a human scream. Tom! I looked over at Ray who also looked concerned. We weren't aware of any other staff members in the building. We knew that if Sunny had been left on his own then Tom was in trouble. He just didn't seem to know his own strength. Another scream and Ray headed for the door.

'Let's go down!' I followed, although I wasn't sure what we were going to do. It seemed that in front of an audience,

Stan got worse. Just as we reached the middle floor we heard the sound of someone running up. It was Tom, breathless and harassed.

'Fat bastard, I'm sick of him, the fat bastard!'

'Shh!' I tried to calm him, pulling him towards the stairs. The last thing we needed, was Stan to hear Tom slagging him off. Ray was laughing. Tom's mood was right down his street.

'Yeah, Tom, yeah. One day we'll return it to him?'

'Fucking hell, Ray, why don't you shout louder!'

I was getting worried. Tom was angry and not thinking and Ray was enjoying egging him on for his own amusement. Getting them both inside our bedroom was a relief. Tom's attention was soon drawn to the day's acquired items. Fifteen brand new pairs of trousers courtesy of Liverpool's department stores.

Thou Shalt Not Steal

I knew we were trying to be too clever but at the time I had too much money and was too stoned to care. Despite my promise to myself, I could nearly smoke a whole joint on my own now. I'd be incapable of any movement afterwards but the feeling was great.

It was one of those days when I'd been smoking myself silly. Lying on my bed, my mind was analysing a million and one things. One was Ray Cooder. He kept calling me 'Uncle Tom' saying I even sounded like a white man. Tom had agreed with him. I began to try and imitate Vinny Graham. This meant I had to put 'man' on the end of my sentences, instead of 'la'. Sometimes he even said 'la' himself but it was the 'man' bit I had to master.

'Hey, man, that's safe, man. You alright, man? Yeah, man!' I began to go over these phrases inside my head.

I didn't hear the door open but suddenly, the gross figure of Stanley Sunny was looming over me.

'Now then!'

'Shit.' I just didn't need this right now. 'Yeah, what's up, mate?'

'Mate! You've been smoking that shit ain't yer? Where's that Tom?' This brought me out of my drug-induced daze. I had to get a grip. He was glaring at me. Both Ray and Tom were out. Vinny was on duty but Stan lived here with us. He was always here. I began to smile at him.

'Look at yer grinning like a fool. I hope there's no drugs in here. You wait here!'

'Oh shit!' Somehow, I knew I was in trouble. Stan returned quickly, accompanied by Vinny, who entered the room shaking his head.

'What have you been up to?'

'Nothing, Vin!'

'We'll find that out, won't we!' sneered Sunny. 'Empty yer pockets.' I knew I was okay doing this because Tom had taken what was left of the weed. Realising I had no more than ten Benson and a lighter, Stanley's attention was drawn to my wardrobe. That's when I began to sweat. Opening it, he observed the neat row of different-coloured trousers: pinstripes, cords, denims and jeans. I could see he was deep in thought. Seeing him close the wardrobe door was a great relief.

'Okay, let's see what yer room mates are hiding!' I began to smile, suppressing the urge to start laughing. Stan headed straight for Tom's wardrobe. It took him and Vinny no more than five minutes to empty all three wardrobes. There was now a mountain of brand new pants on the bedroom floor. Vinny kept chuckling every time Stan's back was turned. I wasn't laughing anymore because I'd have to explain to the others how Fat Boy had discovered the pants. It was all quite simple really. None of us could have afforded to have bought so many pairs at one time.

We were soon visited by Maria O'Bannion, who worked at Merseyside Community Relations in Mount Pleasant, near the city centre. Maria was part of the management committee. I don't really know why she was sent for. I think Stan had designs on getting rid of someone. However, to get rid of Ray, he'd have to get rid of all of us, so a different solution had been found. It was decided that the clothing should be returned to the stores it was taken from and we were banned from going into the city centre for a week. A curfew was also imposed which meant we had to be indoors by eight o'clock.

Ray was cursing. He wanted to go out on Saturday night. He'd promised to show us a great club he was going to called the Babaloo. Tom maintained he'd also been once but Ray laughed at him, saying that he wouldn't get in. A small argument began but since we weren't going anywhere, I suggested they were wasting their energy. The only person who seemed to be happy that we were grounded was Desramona. I began to see why after a week of the curfew. She'd never had so much attention in her life. The rivalry for her attention was on between Tom and Ray. I knew Tom would win. Cooder was too critical and often made her the brunt of his joker's hour when he'd make everyone laugh until they cried, at someone else's expense. He was good at that and everyone joined in, until it was their turn.

We spent most of our time playing card games. It was during a card game that I met Ray's younger brother, Neil. He'd come to visit and had beaten me at blackjack. We had started at a pound but quickly reached five. I was devastated. I promised I'd pay him when my giro came.

Bedtimes were the worst because we were spending too much time together. Ray was beginning to get on my nerves and so was Stanley. I decided to try and work my way into his circle. I wasn't sure how or why his wife Margaret had become his wife. She was so young and pleasant and I noticed how possessive he was of her. I felt sorry for her, she was pregnant again with her third and, if Stephen was anything to go by, she was in for a handful. By playing the naive, lost boy, I managed to move in behind Stan's defences. Ray Cooder couldn't understand my motives, calling me a 'suck hole' but things began to happen a few weeks later that made me glad I'd made the right moves.

Oppression

I failed all my exams but at the time I didn't really care. I had far more adventurous things on my mind. Things were changing at Ujamma House. Stanley's wife now had three sons to look after and Desramona was the live-in babysitter. His alsatians had also had another litter of pups, an event that didn't make him any happier. He was throwing his weight around even more frequently now. Tom had been thrown out; he had got a white girl pregnant and had been pressured into setting up his own home. I was sorry to see him go the way he did, although I think he was glad to be out of Stan's grasp.

I began to hang around with Ray Cooder and his brother Neil. Neil lived in a flat off Grove Street with his girlfriend and baby daughter. I was surprised when I visited his house for the first time; there were so many lads crowded into his living room in a huge cloud of ganja smoke. Everyone in the room was smoking a joint and Ray was in his element. Most of the other lads in the room seemed to have plenty of money. They were discussing going for a slap-up meal in town, the main argument being whether it should be Chinese or Indian. Ray and his brother didn't join in the discussion because, although Neil sold ganja, they were both broke.

'I say we go to the Maharaja'

'Na, Chinatown!'

'Brownie, you make the final decision, lad!' I'd met Brownie once before. I didn't let on that I knew him and neither did he. On the occasion that we'd met, it had been dark and we hadn't had the opportunity to shake hands.

It all happened one cold evening. Having been sent to the shop to buy cigarettes for Margaret and Stanley Sunny, I rode from Lodge Lane towards Kingsley Road. It was past ten o'clock, so I had to travel to Granby Street. I was fortunate in that one of the Arab shops and the off licence on the other block were still open. Having purchased the cigarettes, I left the shop. It was as I mounted the rusty bike that I noticed a small gang of lads. They'd just exited the off licence and were walking towards the shop. A private hire taxi drew up alongside the curb and a middle-aged white guy stumbled out onto the pavement. He looked like he'd had a drink already. I didn't know him, so didn't pay him much attention, until the small firm of lads approached him. I was about to go home but the opening line from one of the lads made me stop:

'Hey, mister, where you going, hey?' If the man was drunk, he soon sobered up as the small gang surrounded him.

'You lot, you can fuck off. Go on, I'll have yer!' he began to rant, moving towards the lad who spoke to him.

He began to take swings at them all and the lads, realising that he would 'have a go', began to retreat out of his way. I saw the look of victory on the man's face as he ambled off around the corner. It just happened to be the corner I was about to take. Watching the gang walk away, I made my move for home. I turned into the street and cycled up behind the same man who'd stood firm against the gang. I'm not sure to this day what he thought I was going to do. Maybe I shouldn't have been riding on the curb. His reactions were quick. Turning, he threw a punch that hit me and knocked me to the ground. The noise from the bike crashing to the pavement, shattered the silence. I was quickly up on my feet. He had his fists up and began to move in again.

'I've told yer, haven't I? Come on then, come on!' he began to hiss.

I was overcome with rage which spelt trouble for him. I'd learnt how to box; Danny Hawksley had taught me that the day he beat me in a fair fight. I begged him to teach me. My right fist shot out, connecting with the man's chin. One, two, Danny had taught me. The second blow hit him full on the nose and I began to dance around him. The flying kick came from nowhere, hitting him full in the chest and sending him crashing to the ground. No, I hadn't kicked him. The lads who had been on his case before had suddenly reappeared and that was the end of the man's resistance. I stood back as they moved in. Like hyenas they waded in, pulling and ripping, pillaging the man, tearing his pants off in their bid to get at his wallet.

'Hit him. Hit him!'

'Come on, I've got it. Let's go!' He sounded like the leader; the same one who had first approached the guy. They began to run towards the mouth of an entry opposite. The white guy they'd just robbed looked in a bad way, so I decided not to stick around.

I'd been wondering all week since the incident who the gang were. I hadn't told anyone else about it. I certainly wouldn't tell Tom, he was trouble enough already. Tom had turned into a kleptomaniac; anything that wasn't tied down became his property.

'Okay, we're going to the Maharaja!' decided Brownie. They soon disappeared and I stayed behind wih Ray and Neil to discuss the five pounds I owed Neil. The conversation soon turned to the lads who'd just left. They were the Berkeley Street Firm. Ghetto boys. On their toes, rough to the core. For them life had always been on the street. Stealing was survival.

I soon began to spend more time with these lads. It was Brownie who remembered the incident on Granby and we laughed about it. Neil's flat became the centre of activity, everyone passed through it and then on to the Red Duster, a public house on the Falkner Street Estate.

Maybe I was moving into bad company but at the time I didn't see it like that. I hated the hostel, mainly because Stan was flying into rages at regular intervals. Maria O'Bannion had been taking more time to observe what was going on. Rumours were circulating that Stan and his family were moving to their own house soon. That would mean the whole of 5 Fern Grove would be for us – no more dogs in the back yard. They always kept us awake at night and Stan would often allow them to run around the house, which meant we had to hide in the bathrooms until he'd finished his little prank and put the dogs back in the yard. It surprised me that he never included cleaning out his dogs' den in our routine chores.

Mushes and Prostitutes

Granby Street, Parliament Street, Grove Street and Princes Avenue were our domain. We'd all been out and bought grey military jackets from a branch of the Army and Navy Stores in Williamson Square. It was Ray Cooder who came up with the idea. For some reason, everyone decided it was a good one and off we went. By wearing the same coats, we had formed ourselves into a street gang. Ray tried to conjure up a name for the newly-formed posse but that wasn't easy because everyone was from a different part of Liverpool. Brownie and the Berkeley Street Boys were Liverpool 8, born and bred. They were about eight strong at the time. From Wavertree came Ray Cooder, his brothers Neil and Jeff, as well as Ricky with his two brothers and a geezer called Eugene. There was also me and a few other lads making us a small force to be reckoned with. There was some rivalry over whether it should be Berkeley or Wavertree who ran things but it was all done in a light-hearted way.

Liverpool 8, as I discovered, had a red light area and, to my surprise, I walked through it every day. Neil's house was on Grove Street and opposite the Falkner Estate was Falkner Square with Canning Street and Huskisson Street running parallel. The little square was sandwiched between both streets. This was all part of the red light district and, therefore, where we used to wait for our prey. Eating in restaurants was expensive, as was smoking as much weed as we were doing and money didn't come easily. That Saturday night, I'd left Fern Grove penniless but decided to go over to Neil's house anyway, as I knew some of the lads were bound to be there. Neil's girlfriend Ann, opened the front door. Neil stood in the hallway.

'Got my fiver yet, Sly?'

'Sly? My name's Rob.'

'Na, I've found a nickname for you ... Sly! Hey, Brownie!' Neil began to move towards his living room. Luckily, Brownie was the only person there. Neil was going to try and make my new nickname stick.

'Yeah, that's a good name for you. Sly, yeah, I like that,' agreed Brownie. I sat down and laughed it off.

Neil told me to roll a spliff. It must have been about ten thirty. It had been cold all evening and I was glad I had somewhere to go, to get away from Ujamma House. By the time I'd rolled the joint, Brownie had lit one, passed it, and was rolling another.

'Fucking hell! Look at that, Sly, that looks like a missile.' Brownie was highly amused by the shape of my amateur joint. Neil swore he'd never ask me to build a spliff again, but I enjoyed smoking it anyway.

By the time we'd come out of our drug-induced slumber, it was nearly three a.m. Neil's girl had already gone to bed. Brownie said he was going home and I decided to leave with him. The street looked desolate and quiet after the weekend.

'Come on, we'll walk this way,' suggested Brownie, as I followed him out onto Grove Street. I was walking a few yards behind him, when he began to point out a distant figure. It was some geezer who looked like he'd just come from Falkner Square. Brownie was already running towards the stranger.

'Come on, it's a mush!' he called to me. I didn't know what he meant but began to run too.

It was a white man. He looked just as shocked as I did when Brownie set on him. Leaping up and throwing a kick at the stranger, Brownie misjudged it and landed on the ground. The man seized his opportunity, not to run but to grab hold of one of Brownie's legs, pulling him and causing a shoe to come off. I was worried that a police car might come up Parliament Street. If that happened, we were nicked. The man now began swinging the shoe in his defence, whilst Brownie was hopping round on one leg.

'Sly, get him, get me shoe, mate!' It wasn't just because I liked Brownie that I jumped into action, I also feared a patrol car turning the corner. I had no choice. The man saw me advancing on him and began to swing at me, the shoe held tightly in his hand.

'You, you … come on, you … you!' That was all I could hear him say.

I remember throwing punches just like Danny had taught me. The man was still putting up a fight, swinging with the shoe. I had to duck, then punch, duck, then punch. I must have blanked out for a while. When I came round, the guy's face was a red mess. He was stumbling around, almost as if he were drunk. I grabbed the shoe, passing it to Brownie.

'Don't let him get away, grab him! Knock him out!' ordered Brownie, fixing his shoe. The guy looked a mess already but Brownie was on him, going through his pockets and pulling out his wares.

We ran, the sound of revving engines not far off, and headed into the Falkner Estate. No one would find us in there in that maze; the whole estate built like a huge fortress. If you didn't know your way around, you would surely get lost. At night, a stranger stood no chance. Once across Parliament Street and into Selbourne Street, Brownie slowed down.

'Stop. Let's share this out, I'm going home!' Quickly opening the wallet, he began to curse as he pulled out two tenners.

'Shit. All that for a tenner each. Shit!' He handed me a tenner and began to set off towards his house.

'Call for me tomorrow,' he shouted as he flew round the corner, 'and you'd best run home!'

I did just that, all the way to Lodge Lane. I was relieved when I reached the gates of number five. Vinny was on duty, so gaining entry wouldn't be a problem. He was alright, Vinny. But the incident wouldn't stop replaying itself in my mind; his face all red with blood. The police might come for me tomorrow – accuse me of murder. I looked again at the ten pound note. I remembered that I was broke, I owed Neil a fiver and could surprise him with it in the morning. I couldn't give it back now, anyway, and the man was only a mush, according to Brownie.

Night Clubs

I'd been going out to the city centre night clubs since my third week at Ujamma House. I think this was one of the reasons I stopped attending school. I was always too tired. Tom had taken me to a local club, called the Yuroba, on the corner of Lodge Lane and Croxteth Road. It was an African-run establishment. At first, we had problems gaining entry, the old Nigerian didn't believe we were old enough to be inside the place. He was right, but Tom had a way with words. The small dance floor would be full by one thirty. The sound of George Clinton and Bootsy Collins hammering from the system: 'One Nation Under a Groove', quickly followed by James Brown.

The crowd would be made up of local people, both mixed race and African. The club belonged to the Yuroba tribe from Nigeria. Their music was loud and tempers fiery. Fights would often break out, mainly between the women fighting for the attentions of a young black African. White girls, no matter how ugly, would find themselves the centre of attention. African students would be out on the hunt for an English wife and would get into confrontations over their girls. Many of them believed that buying a girl a drink, meant you were set up for the night. Not surprisingly, this caused a lot of trouble. It was at these times the police arrived and we would leave before they focused in on us.

It was Ray Cooder who introduced me to the city centre clubs, the Timepiece and the Babaloo. They were in the heart of the city and were the places to be seen. The huge, converted warehouses in the Seel Street area often held 'all nighters', bringing people in from Manchester and Preston. US army personnel from Burtonwood Airbase and sailors from US ships docked in Liverpool helped to make the city centre the place to be. New dances came from across the Atlantic: the Bump, the Shuffle and the Robot. Fresh music would be handed to the club DJ by black American GI's, out in their best uniforms and hats. The competition for the attention of the females would result in at least eight to ten fights. Throughout the evening, bouncers would rush from the Time Piece in Temple Street to the Babaloo, every time a fight broke out and the police were never far away. I'd not had any reason to fight in the clubs. To me, it was a dangerous pastime.

On one occasion, I was so drunk that somebody managed to roll me. I was sporting my brand new, bright-white pants and wide collar shirt and I stumbled into the Timepiece. Having drunk the Babaloo dry of rum and black, my mate handed me a Tennant's and, within minutes, I was hanging over the toilet bowl. The door was closed, but I felt someone pushing his way in. I was absolutely helpless, as he rifled through my pockets. I had thirty pounds on me but I was powerless to save it.

When I recovered, I was hungry. The food was being sold downstairs, the beat still pumping from the speakers. It must have been five am, the place closed at six and I swore that morning, as I walked from the club, tired, smelly and cold, that I'd never get in that state again.

At about this time, I began to search for my identity. I wanted to know where I came from. I also thought it was time I left the hostel. Things were changing, Ray Cooder had been given a flat and was leaving soon. Tom had already gone. Desramona was still babysitting. A new lad Joey had come. He was only sixteen and his dad was white and his mum was black. This was the first time I'd heard of it that way round. Joey was a good lad and we got up to many little scams together but I was still hungry for something, almost pining. I was eighteen and hadn't had sex with a woman. This was beginning to bother me. I hadn't really been interested before but the sudden appearance of Julie Parson had focused my thoughts on the matter.

Julie Parson was a new member of staff. She had taken Pauline's place. Vinny was now deputy, Julie, an assistant. Joey used to say she fancied him but I knew he was fantasising. We were both angry when we found out that Vinny had started dating her. This made me feel awkward and uncomfortable and I soon found myself in a flat in Croxteth Grove. It was only a few blocks away from the hostel and I still spent most of my time there anyway. Trying to detach myself from the hostel was very hard for me. My bedsit was a real mess and lay empty until evening. I'd been given a grant from Dr. Barnado's and I had the dole but the second-hand furniture looked drab and I felt isolated and depressed.

One morning, as I lay on the floor beside the gas fire, I realised that my flat door was being forced. I'd pushed my ancient wardrobe in front of the door as usual, before I went to sleep, because of my fear that someone might break in. Joey sometimes stayed but today he wasn't here. I was alone and scared. The loud banging and cursing voices outside my door made me jump up from the mattress.

'Who's that? Who's that?' I enquired, as I stood trembling in the hallway.

'Police, open this fucking door!' I wasn't sure whether they were police or not but they were nearly in anyway so I moved the wardrobe.

'Right, secure the premises lads,' came a command. 'You! Is anyone else here with you?'

'No,' I replied, still standing in the hallway.

'Okay, you're Rob Suilerman. Is that right?'

'Yeah!'

'Where's your mate, Joey? Well, Rob, I'm arresting you on suspicion of murder!'

'What? What?' All the 'what's' were inside my head as I looked into the face of the man who spoke.

'My name's Detective Sergeant McAteer. Okay get dressed!' I was quickly handcuffed and taken outside. There was an unmarked car waiting for me.'

'Mind yer head,' warned one of the two men who had me sandwiched between them.

It was the first time I'd ever been arrested. Murder, they'd said murder. I didn't know what they were on about. My mind flashed back to the mush. I wondered if Brownie would be joining me but they'd asked about Joey, so I was even more confused.

In no time, we had arrived at Admiral Street. I had been placed inside a room and was asked where I was on that Friday evening. I remembered being with Joey. We were raising money via the fruit machines in local pubs but I couldn't tell them that. Forging the queen's coins was against the law, I knew that. After spending all day in their custody, they decided I could go. Apparently, a man had been killed in a betting office. Because it had happened on Lodge Lane, I believe everyone had been pulled and questioned about it.

On my return to my flat, driven by Sergeant McAteer, I began to feel he was up to something. He kept asking if I was okay, even apologising for my arrest. He told me things were going to crack down in Liverpool 8, boasting that they had been given new powers to combat crime, thanks to the Tories. I wasn't into politics, although I was aware that Labour had lost the General Election. It was the late 1970's and I was nearly nineteen. Getting out of the copper's car was a relief. I tried to stay polite because he was being very polite. He returned the next morning, this time without his firm and rang the bell. I was surprised to see him standing on the step. He asked if he could step in and I obliged, noticing the plastic carrier bag he was holding.

'How are you this morning, Robert?' he asked with a smile. I returned the smile instinctively but my mind told me to be careful. What did he want?

'Oh, I've brought some things for you,' he said, almost reading my thoughts. Handing me the plastic bag, he informed me that it contained items of clothing. He said that he thought I was okay and he'd be back to see me soon. I was concerned straightaway but played along. Taking another look at my one-roomed flat, he said he had to go. I thanked him and he again said I was okay and that he would call again soon. It was with that thought in mind, that I packed my clothes and left. The copper was either after a snout or had something else in mind. Whatever it was, I wasn't going to become his boy. I felt that's what he wanted. I could see it in his eyes.

At first, I went back to 5 Fern Grove. I had to tell one of the staff in Ujamma but when I got there I changed my mind. All the people who now lived there were new except Joey, who was playing football up in Scotland. Stanley Sunny was on duty and I was beginning to panic. Where was I going to go? I couldn't stay. I knew the copper would return. He could make my life difficult. I knew that from watching television and from stories I'd heard.

A week had passed since his second visit and still I hadn't told anyone. The clothes still sat untouched in the plastic bag, in my kitchen. When Vinny or Julie were on duty, I'd find an excuse to stay the night at the hostel but when Stan was on I'd have to return to the bedsit.

One night when Stan had sent me home, I didn't go. Instead, I ventured to Entwistle Heights where all the local lads used to gather in a flat on the twelfth floor. The flat actually belonged to an African boy called Mussifa Osinna who had left home because of parental stress. Most of those who went up there, including the Berkeley lads, were into some kind of criminal activity and I didn't really want to get to involved in what some of them were doing. I also learned that Brownie was in jail.

By half past two, I decided to take the chance and go back to my flat in Croxteth Grove. It was dark and I tried to avoid the local police patrols. They would stop me for the sake of it because a black man was always supposed to be up to something. I was beginning to hate the police. Passing the top of Fern Grove, I could see the lights still burning in the hostel's front room. I wanted to go back in. I knew I'd be safe there but Stan wouldn't let me, not unless I had a good reason. I didn't want to tell him about the copper. I wasn't really sure what he was up to anyway.

By the time I'd thought about all that, I'd reached the mouth of Croxteth Grove. It was dark and quiet. Car windows were iced over. That's when I realised how cold it was. I must have been halfway down, about three doors away from mine, when the car entered the street. My heart stopped. It was a Granada, just like McAteer's. I should have been running by now, but for some reason I just froze.

Escape

It wasn't McAteer driving up the street but the panic the incident created in me was enough. I decided to leave Liverpool and look for my family in Sheffield. The train journey took hours, as did the wait for my bus. It was much colder here, for sure. I had to find my way to Kelvin Flats, the address I'd been given, where my Mum and younger siblings were supposed to be living.

They were surprised to see me. I'd arrived unexpectedly. The return of the prodigal son and all that. For the first time in my life, I felt welcome. Before long, however, things started to deteriorate. My mother had high expectations of me – top priority, get a job. It wasn't that I didn't want one but she'd lined me up in a factory with her brother. My uncle was a good man but the thought of spending my life in a factory reminded me of Frank Purdy. No, I wasn't about to follow his example. This started to cause friction. I was hanging about the estate with the local lads. A cousin of mine called Shannon had introduced me to a couple of people who were involved in petty crime but I decided not to get to involved. On one occasion they'd picked a fight with an opposing gang. We were all in retreat as the fight spilt back onto Kelvin Flats, my mother watching the whole procedure from her balcony. I was in trouble.

I began to stay away from home as much as I could. She was about to move into a new house in a place called Middlewood. Working as a nurse for a local steel factory, my mother regarded herself as middle-class and being the eldest in her family and raised in Jamaica, made her no push-over. She was proving a hard nut to crack. I wondered if she knew how to show affection, I certainly hadn't received any. Maybe she was afraid to show me that she cared, I just couldn't work it out. I was her first born and I felt unwanted.

I started going to the local pub, spending my giros on lager. At the same time, my mum had turned Christian overnight. My two sisters and brother were told to attend church but I wasn't prepared to go and went to the pub instead.

It was a Sunday when they first came into the pub. One was really fat, but the other was shaped like a model. It was my drinking partner who got onto them first. I was a bit inexperienced and shy. There was only the one worth checking out and my mate was already doing just that. I was therefore surprised when she walked over to me.

'Alright?' I managed.

'Where are you from?'

'Liverpool.'

'Liverpool!' she mimicked, 'I love that accent!' We sat and talked for an hour before she left. My mate couldn't hide his disappointment, especially when he learnt that she'd asked me to call at her house later that evening. She said she was decorating and could use a strong pair of hands. This promised to be be my first and I was as nervous as hell.

Her name was Shirley, the fat girl was her sister, Doreen. I thought Shirley would have been alone when I called but Doreen was with her. After putting up a few strips of wallpaper, Shirley sent Doreen to the off licence. Nothing happened while she was gone. I think she wanted it to but I was too tense. Doreen returned with another geezer, older than me and built like a tank. He introduced himself as Lenny. I assumed he was with Doreen but I was wrong. The cans of super-strength lager were passed round by Doreen, who'd also bought a large bottle of vodka and a cheap bottle of wine.

'A party, I love parties!' giggled Shirley, curling up on the couch. Lenny had moved to sit next to her. I began to bite my lip because I felt that my place was next to her.

'Here you are, Rob, have some wine,' invited Doreen, forcing a glass into my empty hand, the liquid already poured. After everyone had been given a glass of wine, Doreen proposed a toast, demanding that we drain our glasses.

'Down the hatch!' she shouted. Before long, we were all laughing. Laughing at everything. Lenny had taken his shirt off and was dancing with Doreen. Shirley had moved from the couch and was gyrating round the room on her own. I was fucked. For some reason, my body wouldn't function. I could still laugh though, but I felt so strange. Without warning, I suddenly found Doreen standing directly in front of me, grinning in my face.

'Come on, Rob, I'm gonna have you tonight, you young buck!' I started to laugh again. Inside, my mind said 'get away, you fat bitch' but the words weren't coming out.

'Did yer like that wine? That one was specially for you. Ha-ha!' I could hear what she said but my body felt so relaxed, so relaxed. I had no resistance in me, I just laughed.

'Come on, Lenny, let's get him up for a dance. Come on!' I didn't want to dance but with the help of Lenny, they pulled me to my feet.

'Shirley, come on, come on!' she shouted, her stale breath in my face. I was being swung around from here to there. I cursed myself because I'd sworn never to get into this state again. It had all happened so quickly, Doreen had tricked me.

'Take yer pants off, Lenny, take 'em off!'

'Take his off – take his off!'

'Na, na – please stop! Stop!' Before I knew it, I was on the deck. The rest of it was like a dream. Doreen was naked, her flabby white breasts inching closer to my face. Shirley and Lenny were on the floor beside us. He was thrusting into her as she moaned with pleasure. Doreen was squatting on top of me, swigging from a bottle.

'D'yer want some, love?' No, I didn't, but the neck of the bottle was shoved into my mouth anyway.

For two days and three nights I was held as some kind of hostage. Lenny left the same night but Doreen wasn't letting me go. I woke up drunk only to be fed more drink; drink that knocked me to sleep. I was still naked and had been dumped on the sofa. Shirley had gone and fat Doreen was abusing me repeatedly at her leisure. When Lenny finally returned, I was awake. He stood over me, scrutinsing me with Doreen. I think they thought I might be dead.

Too much fuckin' Benolin, Doreen, you'll kill him.' I detected the concern in Lenny's voice.

'Yeah, you'd best clean him up and just put him in the pub!' That's where my cousin Shannon found me, on the pavement beside the pub. I stank and my clothes were a mess. Shannon said my sister had been looking all over for me. I had to ask him to take me to his house to clean up, I could smell fat Doreen all over me. I swore I was going to knock the fat bitch out but, for now, I'd have to recover. When I told Shannon what had happened, he laughed and told me they were bondage queens, prostitutes and Lenny was their bisexual pimp. Enough said. I decided to return to my mum's and give Christianity a chance.

The Church of the Pentecostals was rowdy, with black women often going into a frenzy, as they went into the spirit. 'Hallelujah! Praise the Lord,' the choir would sing. The catchy rhythm encouraging the worshippers to join in – 'Hallelujah, Praise the Lord.' I wasn't enjoying myself, I just didn't feel it was right for me but at least my mum was happy. I needed to get a job now, then I might crack the nut. Maybe she would smile at me, perhaps even give me a hug but, as time went by, the more we drifted apart.

It was Saturday in June, 1981, and I was really depressed. My mother had gone into one of her moods and I'd been in my room all day. There was a knock on the door and I heard it opening. It was Sharon, my sister.

'Rob, did yer know, there's riots in Liverpool?'

'No, whereabouts?'

'A place called Toxteth. They just said on the news!'

I was off my bed like a shot. The radio was downstairs and the news was due shortly. She was right, Liverpool was on fire. Newsflashes were coming right through the night. I had my bags packed by Sunday evening, the riots were still continuing and I wanted to be there. I hated Sheffield, I didn't belong there. I didn't tell her I was going, I don't really think she cared. Early Monday morning, I boarded the National Express coach. I was going home, back to Liverpool.

Riots

By the time I arrived, it was Monday and they'd been fighting with the police all weekend. CS gas had been used the previous night. There were crowds of people walking round the manor and reporters from all over the globe had descended on the area, looking for answers.

Parliament Street was a mess and Lodge Lane had been blitzed; most of the shops and businesses looted and burned to the ground. The Rialto Centre was still burning on Parliament Street. The banks had all been pillaged throughout the area including the National Westminster, Barclays and the TSB. None of them escaped. Hi-fi shops had been cleared of their stock up and down Smithdown Road. Other casualties were the local Kwik Save and other neighbouring supermarkets. Not even the Unigate Dairy was spared.

People boasted of having food cupboards full to the brim. Everyone seemed in a party mood. I'd missed out and felt cheated. After walking around for over an hour, I set off for Neil Cooder's flat on Grove Street. He was in, along with a few of the lads. They all looked tired but had plenty of stories to tell. They had been fighting hand to hand with the police. The names of those captured were checked and tallied.

After promising Neil I'd call back, I left the security of his flat. It was getting dark and I needed to get to the hostel. The police were out in force, they'd saturated the area. Walking towards Lodge Lane, I saw the battle lines already drawn. There was going to be more trouble tonight, I could see that. This time I'd be able to get involved. I was excited.

Young Joey met me at the front door. He looked well and began to tell me about his exploits that night.

'Three videos, brand new in the box, Robbie, honest!'

'And the bizzies took them, kidder?'

'Yeah, this morning they was all over the place. I hid them in the entry. Anyway, I've got some champagne upstairs, come up after!'

'Okay, who's on duty?'

'A new guy, Ray, he's alright. You looking to stay?'

'Yeah.'

The Sunnys had moved into a new house at the top of Lodge Lane. This meant there was more space for the residents. Entering the office, which was now downstairs in Stanley Sunny's old bedroom, Ray, small and of mixed-race, said he would allow me to stay but I'd have to see Stanley, who was still the warden, in the morning. I thanked him, before taking my suitcase upstairs. I was glad to get my old room back. There was another guy in there, Darren Blyth, who seemed okay at first. Anyway, Joe was soon in and pouring champagne into a cup.

'Ray won't let us go out tonight, Rob!'

'Stanley's left orders.'

'Shit! Shit!' I would have to slip out now. I'd tell him I had to see someone. Anyway, I was old enough to do my own thing.

Eight thirty and I was again walking towards the trouble spot, Parliament Street. I was on my way to Neil's but the fracas taking place had drawn me in. The police were in small black jeeps, with large spotlights mounted on the roofs. I saw lads that I knew but everyone seemed to be on the retreat, moving back towards Granby Street. I needed to be going the other way, towards Grove Street. As I looked across Parliament Street, I could see the large police presence.

'Yo, Sly!'

'Yo, Kelly, what's happening?' It was Terry Kelly, one of the Berkeley lads.

'Best get out of here, mate, they've got guns and that in the jeeps. They're snatch squads, if they come, run!' He was already running. A jeep appeared over the grass verge, people were running from its path. Girls were screaming abuse as the vans drove by, chasing the menfolk. I was running towards Granby Street, where there was plenty of cover; entries and alleyways that ran all over the manor. There was also the Falkner Estate but it was on the other side of Parliament Street and the police had cut off all access to the so-called 'fortress'.

Most people thought they'd reached safety but we were

still being pursued by the blacked-out jeeps. Chasing people onto Granby Street, the police began to leave their vehicles and enter the alleyways. Wielding batons and smacking anyone in their path, they began their offensive. Reaching the safety of a building belonging to an old friend, I watched from an upstairs window.

'They're not regular police, you all know that. Look at them!' That was a guy called T.J., who was being hailed as a general. I knew T.J. from his visits to the hostel. He was a karate instructor now – a black belt, third dan. He hated the police and had been leading many of the attacks against them. Judah, whose premises we presently occupied, also seemed concerned about reports of an SAS man in the manor.

'Bet them pigs are from Ireland, I'll put money on it!' he announced. I knew that it was getting late and I had to return to the hostel. T.J. was also going out, despite the protests from the others. I decided to chance it and leave too.

'You two are crazy. If they catch hold of yer, you know the score!' warned Judah.

'Listen, Judah, just tell Milesy and Tosh, if they're not nicked already, to call it a night!'

'Okay, T.J., easy as yer go.' I was already outside the door. T.J. moved off towards the mouth of the nearest entry, I was right behind.

'Where are you going, Sly?'

'Lodge Lane, mate.'

'I'm going to Parliament Place, you can come if yer want.'

'Na, I've got to go back.'

'Oh yeah, you're in that hostel, aren't yer?'

'Yeah!'

After moving back into the crowds, we exited onto Princes Road. T.J. departed and walked towards the Dingle. I headed towards Bentley Road.

Ujamma House

Riots continued throughout the week but gradually the police regained control. Many of the local lads had been arrested, others had been injured by CS gas canisters and rubber bullets. There was talk of a boy being killed. After hearing some of the things that had taken place inside the police cells, I gave thanks that I hadn't been captured.

I'd spoken to Stanley Sunny about my situation. At first he laughed, mainly because I'd failed in my attempts to go it alone. He agreed I could stay, which made me the oldest and longest-serving resident at Ujamma House. It was mid-1981 and I was back at square one in the hostel, a non-starter. I decided to 'locks' my hair. Neil Cooder, who I was hanging out with, was also 'locksing up', a Rastafarian thing.

The hostel was changing hands after Stanley Sunny resigned. I didn't know the reason why but thought it was about time. Anyway, our new warden came in the shape of a Cockney, by the name of Gideon Rupert. He was a part-time musician and seemed okay at first, until he began embezzling the funds and he too had to go.

Vinny had left and so had Julie. A new guy called Trevor James began working at the place. I was surprised to see him, because I'd been on 'Community Industries' with him, which made us virtually the same age. Trevor had the longest dreadlocks I'd ever seen. He was joined by another geezer called Tony Mantelpiece, a real funny man who should have taken up a stage career.

We spent a couple of months without a warden. Members of the Community Relations Council were searching hard for the right person; they'd already made two mistakes so this time they'd have to take more care, the reputation of the hostel for homeless black youths was at stake. Enter J.J. James – a local born black guy – whose reputation preceded him. He was a local hero back from the days of the skinhead wars. Although he'd been jailed for a fight at the ice rink, he was now an upstanding citizen, or so they thought. J.J. James was now in charge of 5 Fern Grove.

It wasn't long before I was offered another flat. This time it was a proper one with a bedroom and a living room, just what I wanted and I soon moved in. I decided to approach J.J. and ask if I could perhaps work at Ujamma on a part-time basis. He said I could do some voluntary work and I agreed. Along with Trevor Jones and Tony Mantelpiece, I became a sort of staff member. The residents were all new by now. Joey had left, as had most of the people who'd been there in his era. We had a new influx of residents including Darren Blyth's younger brother Arran and two girls who shared a bedroom downstairs. Soon after, Tony Simons, the only white lad to stay at Ujamma arrived. Martin Allan, another mixed-race lad who reminded me straightaway of Markie, arrived from a home in Southport.

It wasn't long before the post I covered came up for interview. Maria O'Bannion and members of the management team were conducting the interviews for the vacant post. On the day I received the good news and became a fully-paid staff member, Eddie Edwards arrived. Along with Martin Allan, he became a real handful but I had something in common with both of them, I'd been through the system and they respected that. I soon became more than just a member of staff, I was more like a big brother. I knew everything that went on, good and bad, which gave them someone they could confide in, who wasn't a stranger to their situation. I'd been through the care system, parentless. Now twenty-two, I had the responsibility of guiding others.

Throughout a year involved in the running of Ujamma and its internal politics, I'd kept in contact with Neil Cooder. Neil had teamed up with a guy called Carlos and I began to spend time out of working hours with them on Granby Street. Granby Street was now known as the Frontline.

Things were hotting up at the Frontline. I'd been away on a holiday with the residents of Ujamma when I missed out on the sting of the year. The two men, who came from Scotland, carrying cases full of cannabis, thought they'd come to do business. The Frontline Posse had different ideas! I'm not quite sure exactly what happened but, thanks to the two Scots, they were soon in a position to buy a building on the corner of Cawdor Street and Granby Street. It had been the betting shop and needed a lot of work so, week in, week out, the Frontline Posse worked on the building. The new arcade-come-pool room inside the renovated bookies became a success. Carlos and Neil were joined by another three local guys, the Chinaman, Judah and Bunny Lion. I was Neil's friend and therefore automatically part of the team. Despite his name, the Chinaman was of mixed-race and a herbalist. He knew, just from looking, how to tell good ganja from bad ganja and, in the business we were in, that was an asset.

My dreadlocks were growing now, I had a sense of belonging and, with my time fully-occupied between Ujamma House and The Frontline, I was happy. I even learned to drive and bought myself a second-hand car. It was around the same time that Ujamma House had been given a new building on Hartington Road. There had also been another change of leadership. J.J. James had been up to all kinds of scams. Old habits die hard; he too had begun to mess with the books. Tony Mantelpiece was made warden in charge, Trevor Jones, his deputy. The new house was perfect; originally five flats, the two on the ground floor became communal areas, including the staff office and bedroom, residents' kitchen, living room and washroom. Upstairs were the residents' sleeping quarters; private rooms with their own key. Ujamma House was functioning properly, for now.

I became involved with selling ganja. Not that I needed to really, but I did smoke it and, to keep my habit, I sold it. Granby Street was still a 'no go' area for the police and we could sell ganja almost openly. It wasn't long before young Martin Allan joined me. He had a family in the area and was younger than me and tended to do his own thing. I'd watched him since his arrival at Ujamma, wild and confused. The day I caught him sniffing butane gas, marked the beginning of our friendship. I had to let him know that it wasn't right, even though others had already told him. His response to me telling him was different.

'I want to try everything!' he told me. I explained that

'everything' wasn't always good by giving examples from when I was in the kids' home, like how a boy had once decided to try hanging off a window ledge. I didn't have to finish, he began laughing. I suggested we smoked a spliff and chill out and, under the influence of marijuana, we talked over our problems and situations. From then on, we always looked out for each other.

It wasn't long before we were regularly joined in such meetings by Eddie Edwards and Tony Simons. I made them swear not to tell the other staff members. If they knew I was smoking with the residents, I'd be out of a job. They agreed to say 'nish'. Three weeks later, Martin confessed that they'd also smoked a joint with Trevor when he was on a shift. Well, that didn't surprise me but funny Tony Mantelpiece had also smoked a joint with the lads. Soon, house meetings were held upstairs after ten o'clock. At the top of our agenda would be the supply of Rizla and cigarettes. When two or three joints were in circulation, Tony would begin his comedy act. Eyes would swell with tears of laughter before he'd finished his tales. The upstairs light in the back room would burn well into the twilight hours.

Trevor and Tony soon fell out over something and Trevor ended up resigning. After a few days of talking him round, he returned. I was glad, because he brought a bit of culture to the place. I had been made deputy to Mantelpiece. Trevor didn't mind, we always got on well together, so titles didn't matter. I began to understand why Trevor didn't like Tony, it was his attitude to work. Trevor was a Rastafarian and held to their strong beliefs about what was right and wrong, whereas Tony was a fly-by-night. I respected Trevor because he always brought some sense to a situation when things got out of hand but I also liked Tony Mantelpiece who always had me in stitches, so I decided to stay neutral.

The Frontline Posse had made some progress, the building looked almost complete but I began to dislike their internal politics and initiated my separation from them. Neil was no longer a part of it, having fallen out with Carlos and the Chinaman. His brother Ray, was spraying all the street signs red, yellow and green. I would occasionally see him and we'd acknowledge each other but Ray Cooder was on a mission, so I left him to it. Seeing him made me think of Tom. I hadn't seen him for years. Someone told me he'd moved to London. I wondered if he'd ever made it back to his father's country, Uganda, like he'd always said he would.

A Daughter

I got caught in a downpour of rain returning from Granby Street, I hadn't even reached the middle of Bentley Road and I was drenched. That's when I realised that Darren Blyth's sister lived close by. I knocked at her door, number fifteen, flat two. Thankfully she was in, and allowed me to step inside.

She invited me in and told me to sit by the fire. I'd met her before and she made me feel at home straightaway. After fixing me a cup of tea and sitting down, the crying of her baby daughter from the bedroom told me we weren't alone.

I don't know whether I really fancied Angela Blyth but I ended up having sex with her that evening. I don't remember whether or not I wore a condom. Anyway, I enjoyed it and returned the following night. It wasn't long before I moved in and she was pregnant again, this time with my child. She often complained that I didn't know how to show her any love, that I spent too much time out with my mates. The closer it got to her giving birth, the worse her rantings became.

Angela also had a younger sister called Dione. Although only a couple of years younger, Dione was very timid. In November, 1984, Angela gave birth to my daughter Sarah. I was sort of happy and so was Dione who started coming round to help Angela.

Not long after she'd given birth, Angela went away, taking both of the kids with her. I was left on my own for a whole week, so on the second night, I went out with the lads

– all night blues and early Sunday morning breakfast. Leaving my mates at the end of the street, I saw Dione on her way to Angela's house.

'Oh, I've left my dole card!' she explained. She'd called yesterday but I wasn't in. On opening the door, we were overcome by the smell of stale socks and unwashed dishes. Dione looked at me.

'How long's Angie been gone then? Two days, and look at the state!' She automatically began to pick things up around the front room.

'Okay, I'll have a cup of tea, Dee – nice one!'

'I'm not making tea!'

'Ah, come on, you can see I can't cope on me own. Anyway, I'm tired!'

'Go to bed then, I'll clean the place up!'

'Nice one, Dione,' I winked.

She smiled. I got undressed and jumped into bed. I must have slept a little because when I woke up it was dark again. The front door bell was ringing. Grabbing a towel to cover myself, I rushed to the door. It was Dione.

'Oh, I thought I'd best come and wake you up, lazy bones!'

'Nice one, Dione,' I replied sarcastically, 'shut the door and come in!'

'You mean, come in and shut the door!'

'Yeah, that one,' I was still half asleep. It did cross my mind to put some pants on but I didn't. I entered the living room and plonked myself down on the sofa

'Turn the telly on Dione, please, oh and I'd love a cuppa.'

'You're too cheeky, I don't know how Angie copes with you!'

'I suppose you could find out!'

I don't know why that slipped out but it did. It didn't cross my mind to have sex with Dione, she was of age but she was also Angela's sister. She pretended not to hear me but I knew she had. Dione never went home that evening. I know I didn't wear a condom, I didn't have one but I didn't think I'd allowed my seed to penetrate her. We said nothing about what we'd done. Angela came home and stayed. That was until Dione began to show signs of pregnancy.

'Oh, Dione must have a boyfriend on the sly, you know!'
'Do yer think so?'
'Yeah, she's pregnant!' I lay next to Angela trying to keep my heart rate steady. Dione pregnant – and no boyfriends. I knew she didn't have one and I knew she hadn't had one. Shit! My head was in turmoil but I decided to play along.

'It might be that boy, er, what's his name?' Angela seemed to know who I was talking about.

Although my daughter Sarah was beautiful and I was proud of her, I began to get into conflicts with Angela. Somehow I think she began to get suspicious of me and her sister. Anyway, it wasn't long after the arrival of Dione's baby son that all was revealed.

On The Run

My fortunes had taken a turn for the worse and now I was really in a mess. The squat I was in was cold, cold and empty; the city of London, a big lonely place. Trevor was supposed to be here as well but he'd got a job cooking for a pop group who were on tour. I knew they were in Bristol and not due back in London for a few days. I was broke. I'd left my security job guarding an empty block of offices. It wasn't my idea of fun – but right now, I sure could have used the money.

My second raw potato tasted worse than the first. I went back to bed, it must have been about four but the traffic on Tooting High Street never stopped. Tooting Bec, London, SW 17. How did I come to be here?

It all seemed to have happened at once, all the bad luck, Dione giving birth to a son and Angela finding out that I was the father. Angela and her sister argued and fought and the family began to get involved. I'd already left my daughter's house – Angela was adamant about that. It took me a long time to appreciate that what I had done was wrong.

Having moved into the Frontline on Granby Street, things got worse. Every day was like a movie show: fights, screams, loud music, gambling, stolen cars and property, hard drugs and soft junkies. Gangsters, pimps and hustlers, everyone passed through the Frontline. Unfortunately, some of us lived there, for a while anyway.

At least I had my job. I was still deputy to Tony Mantelpiece. He and I were getting on really well, so I'd decided to start up my own enterprise, just like Maggie had suggested. I decided that if they could sell ganja on Granby, then I could sell it elsewhere. The problem was where? It wasn't a problem for long. In my blindness, Ujamma house became the prime spot. Things were going well and, together with one of my residents, we began to serve sticks of black ash. In fact, things were going so well that I became complacent. I forgot to tell our ever-increasing number of customers not to call when we weren't in. When they did, Tony approached me.

'Robbie, la, we can't have them knocking yer know, yer on top!'

'You're on top, the price you charged me for the last lot!'

'Fuck off, that was good gear, that!'

'What are you doing here anyway?'

'Staff meeting and O'Bannion's coming. Robbie make sure no one knocks!' I got one of the residents to sit in the car outside. Anyone who looked like they were approaching had to be stopped and served down the road. I was smart you see, or so I thought.

The introduction of a new staff member saw my seven year reign at Ujamma come to an end. Unknown to me, Shelley O'Donnel was Ms O'Bannion's sister and for three shifts on the run, she'd answered the door on several occasions.

'Excuse me, can I have a five pound draw!

She sat across the room from me as I was confronted about the issue. Of course, I didn't have a clue why people should call for ganja here, must be one of those kids I suggested. No, they weren't buying that. Ms. O'Bannion and her senior had asked to see me the following day and I knew it was curtains. The evidence was slim and I admitted nothing but the choice put before me was to resign or be dismissed so I agreed to resign. I was now unemployed and living on the Frontline, rapidly heading for trouble.

I still had my motor, a blue Fiat which I could park off Cawdor Street to sell my weed. Having dreadlocks helped, white people always asked Rastas for ganja. I got to see more of Martin Allan and Eddie, who had since left Ujamma. They too were trying to survive out on the streets but there was too much competition. Living on the top floor of the Frontline Café gave me the advantage of being on the street first every morning and it was on one of those mornings when I was surprised to see Martin so early.

'What's happening, lad?' He had a look in his eye. A look I knew well.

'Nothin' Al, I'm skint!'

'So are me and Eddie!'

'And what?'

'Got a plan, ain't we?'

'Have we?'

'Yeah, you in?'

Putting on a black balaclava over my dreadlocks was difficult, I began to sweat before we'd even begun our practice run inside Eddie's flat.

'I can see fuck all with this!'

'You look the part though. Come on, let's do it!'

Of course, even that didn't go right. I steamed into the place, waving a 'rep'. Everyone hit the floor. My mate was on the till and I had everyone else covered.

'Come on, come on!' I shouted, panic setting in.

'Where's the rest of the bloody money? Where's the..?'

'Forget it. Go! Go!' We were out, running towards the getaway. I was in first but my face mask was already off because I couldn't breathe.

'Fuckin' hell, put it on. Fuckin' hell!'

When we got back to the safety of the flat we were devastated. Our robbery had only produced thirty-five pounds. It wasn't until I returned to Granby to spend my share, that someone approached me.

'That was you that!'

'Me what?'

'Did that skank this morning!'

'What skank?' I was fortunate that it was only one of the lads but I couldn't be sure that nobody else had recognised me. I rushed off to Dione's flat and began to cut off my dreadlocks.

'Why are you cutting them off?'

'I just am, go see to the baby!'

'He's sleeping, you been doing something, ain't yer?'

'Dione, what have I told yer? Don't start prying into me business!'

'Me brother was round today. He wants to fight yer.'

'Oh shit, that's all I need!' That was it, I'd had enough. My head felt as if it was going to explode and I needed advice.

'Trevor, I've got heavy problems, mate!' Trevor, who'd now changed his name to Gad, was a true Rastafarian whose dreadlocks had grown to touch the floor. He had become my imam. He listened and advised.

'I'm leaving Liverpool soon!'

'The hostel, you going to give up work?'

'Yeah, it's gone downhill since you left, all the wrong you did those last days, didn't replace the good you did before. You possess a talent for working with young people. You've slipped from your path, you need to get back on it.' It may have been the ganja talking but his words lifted me. He opened my eyes to what I was doing, where I was heading.

'I have a place ready in London, it's up to you, you can go tomorrow.'

'What will I do?'

'There's enough work in London, man. More, than enough!'

He was right, there was enough work in London but the pay for all the hours was no good. Why had I picked security work? Now, I couldn't sign on for six weeks, my weekly travel pass had run out and I was starving. That's when my mind turned to the Common, Tooting Common. It was dark and people walked through there to get home. Maybe I should accost someone, rob them, but then I might get caught. I didn't want to go to prison.

It must have been about ten pm, time for some more potatoes. I was ravenous, the cupboards bare. I looked out of the window and noticed a car pulling up next door, a large blue Mercedes. My eyes turned to their living room and kitchen. There was plenty of food in there, I could see it. They were having a late dinner, suits and ties. I suppose I could wait until later and maybe burgle the place. Yeah, things were that bad.

Bouncing Back

I felt sick. It had been days since I'd been anywhere, not even out of the bedroom. My beard had grown as thick as the fungus between my toes. I could smell putrid raw potatoes, the ones that were scattered about the bed. The room stank, I must have vomited at some time. I could barely focus. The room was spinning so I closed my eyes. During those hours, I had visions of people in the room, people talking, a woman and, it seemed, Trevor.

'Robbie, Robbie!' Trevor's voice. I opened my eyes. The room was empty. This made me angry. Someone was playing tricks on me. I rolled myself off the bed and onto the rug, crying from the pain in my stomach. Crawling on my knees, I moved slowly towards the door. I didn't make it, too much movement and more liquid rushed from my mouth. I lay uncovered on the floor, I'd forgotten to drag a blanket along with me and I began to shiver from the cold.

The sudden tremors I felt in the floor just seemed like another of my symptoms but the sudden rush of fresh air wasn't. Trevor had returned. The tour had been cut short.

After nursing me back to fitness, my friend taught me how to cook fish and rice. I felt I'd been given a second chance and, in a new frame of mind, I began to search for work; the work I enjoyed doing best. Following Gad's suggestion, I took my references from Ujamma to an agency who soon found me work in an adolescent unit in South

London.

Barnes Hall Adolescent Unit was out in the sticks. Gad was also going to be working there but wasn't due to start until the following week. We had been interviewed and shown around the home and the manager, Nick Merry, had explained why he'd requested two black male staff – they were having problems.

'We have three black kids here,' explained Nick. 'Tanya Roberts, she's a pleasant girl, when she wants to be. Then there's Sarah Beckford and her brother Wayne, now this is where the problem is. Wayne's twelve and does as he pleases. Anyway, you'll see!'

I was introduced to an Irish girl called Margaret who also worked for an agency and would be working my first shift with me. There was also a white hippy-type geezer called Adam who had been given the responsibility of 'key working' Wayne Beckford. 'Key working' meant that you saw to that child's needs and liaisons with field social workers.

The house was quiet. The kids had gone to the picture house in Hammersmith so I sat on the kitchen stool being entertained by Amy, the cook, a small Jamaican woman who I took to at once. I liked her even more when I saw she had more control over the kids than Nick and it wasn't long before I nicknamed her 'Ma'.

I had to make a success of my first meeting with the kids when they got back. I was twenty-seven and felt nervous. I had to pull this off. I knew the kids were younger than the ones I was used to looking after at the hostel. Tanya came in first. A big girl, aged thirteen, she weighed about fifteen stone but with the face of an angel. Putting on her airs and graces, she disappeared upstairs.

'Tanya, she a bad one when she start,' said Amy, slicing through a large onion.

Sarah Beckford came in next, the most beautiful black girl I'd ever seen. Sarah was fifteen and eyed me up suspiciously. Her brother, a short-arsed little black-faced boy followed her. He paid me no attention as he made his way upstairs.

Everything seemed to be going nicely until evening time. It was after ten and Margaret and Adam had told all the kids to come into the house. I noticed that Tanya and Sarah had been drinking alcohol. Amy the cook, had long gone, and the kid gloves were off.

'Hey you, fuckin' Margaret. I'm not going to bed yer know!' came the voice of large Tanya with Sarah standing beside her, giggling.

'Come on now, girls, let's not show off, up to bed now!' pleaded Margaret.

'I said no, I'm not fuckin' going!' shouted Tanya.

I began to feel awkward. Tanya was smiling at me, as if to show me what power she had. I smiled back and returned to the kitchen door. Adam was carrying Wayne who was drunk, across the front garden. Reaching the kitchen, Adam headed with him towards the stairs.

'Stop, hey fuckin' put me down. Now, I said!'

'No, Wayne, I'm taking you to bed!' At that, the boy turned into a devil. I stood in amazement as he began to kick wildly. Adam let him go.

'Okay, Wayne, okay. Stop it. Calm down, calm down.'

'Just get yer smelly breath out me fuckin' face, I'm gettin' me supper!' with that, Wayne stumbled back towards the kitchen.

I said nothing as the tirade of abuse and defiance continued until almost midnight. I couldn't find much to say to Margaret and Adam before we turned in. Margaret looked whacked and Adam looked exactly the same as when I had first met him, a laid-back hippy. He had two tins of beer in his overnight bag and asked if I wanted one. I declined his offer and decided to call it a night.

The following morning, Adam gave me a call at seven thirty.

'Mornin' Rob, here's a cuppa, I'm gonna wake the kids for school!'

'Okay, mate, I'll be down soon!'

I had to go and look at a flat in Wandsworth that afternoon. My shift finished at twelve, which gave me time to get to Wandsworth by two. First, the kids had to be sent off to school. It wasn't until I'd helped myself to the toast that Margaret had made, that I noticed that not all the kids were there.

'Where's Wayne and the two girls?' I enquired.

'Oh! They don't attend school, expelled, they'll be getting private tuition.'

'I see!'

It wasn't until ten that Nick, the manager, arrived. He had a cup of tea before asking why the other kids were still in bed. I wanted to suggest a hangover but remained silent while Adam and Margaret scuttled upstairs to wake them. Tanya's voice was the loudest. Amy arrived and just shrugged, to her it was normal procedure.

'Them can't get them youth up, it's the same every morning. Don't know why them try, listen them!' I could hear, as could the whole neighbourhood. It was Tanya.

'GET OUT ME FUCKIN' ROOM ... OUT ... OUT!' Nick was out of his office and heading upstairs. I followed and, reaching the landing, I could see Margaret standing by an open door.

'Tanya. Tanya, you must get up. I've asked you nicely!'

'Just fuck off!' came the reply. By now, Nick had reached the doorway and I stood behind him wondering how he was going to handle the situation.

'Tanya, did you swear then? Did you? What did we promise the other day? You know what this means, don't you? That's your allowance down again this week. Now come on, get up, do as you're asked!' Tanya's response was to turn over to face the wall. Nick nodded his head at Margaret.

'Leave her, she knows she's in trouble. Are Sarah and Wayne up?'

'I think Adam's getting them up, Nick.'

'Good!' he replied, heading back towards the stairs. I looked at Margaret, she shrugged. I shrugged, it seemed to be the 'in' thing to do.

I was happy that Nick let me go early, I had a lot to do that afternoon. My next shift would be in two days, I was looking forward to the challenge. I'd have to tell Gad what to expect. Those kids were running things their way. This was going to be a tough one.

Gaining Control

The flat I was given was in Earlsfield, Wandsworth. I hadn't realised that the famous jail was up the road until I had the misfortune of visiting the place. I was happy with my flat, it was my own and that's what I needed. Gad had moved into a flat share with another scouser, Jimmy, who'd come to the big city to study.

On my return to work, I was informed that a window had been smashed and the fire extinguisher emptied. Wayne was believed to have been the culprit. I had been joined again by Adam and Margaret and this time I swore things would run differently. Again, I spent most of the day in the kitchen with Amy. If anyone could tell me what was what, then it was the cook, I knew that, I'd been raised in these places. Most of the kids had been watching me all day. I stayed reserved for now, waiting for an opportunity to show myself.

It was a regular occurrence for things to go haywire at bedtime. This time, the two girls were already indoors but Adam was at the front door, trying to coax Wayne inside. I decided to give it a go.

'Hey, lad!' I shouted, reaching the front door, 'time to come in now!' I heard him laugh, before approaching from the shadows.

'I ain't going to bed, yet!' he informed us, brushing his way past.

'If we ask you to, you will,' I insisted, as he entered the house.

That's when he ran. I didn't know where he was going to, until Adam shouted; 'The fire escape, he's going for the fire door.'

I bolted after him but he was quick and he'd already reached the fire door. The shrill blast of the alarm told me he'd broken the seal and I continued chasing him. I could see him outside, dashing across the back garden. I was closing down on him, the fence was looming up. He was over, so was I. He could feel me now, almost breathing down his neck and I sensed his panic. He knew he wasn't getting away. My hand touched his jacket, then I grabbed him.

'G-g-get off. G-g-get off me', he panted. 'Who the fuck are you? Get off!' At that point, I threw him against the wall.

'Who the fuck do you think you're chattin' to, hey? Making me run like that, I should kick you up.'

'What? You can't talk to......!'

'Hey, you think I'm a white man or something? Don't fuckin' take the piss out of me and we'll get along just fine!'

I grabbed him and began to pull him towards the house. He was subdued until we reached the front door. Tanya and Sarah had come to see who'd won the confrontation. As soon as he saw them he started again.

'Get the fuck off me, you. Sis, get him off!'

Sarah sniggered.

'Wayne, just come in now anyway,' she wisely suggested.

'Okay, but let me go!'

'I will, but run again, I'll catch yer and the next time, mate...'

'I can have my supper though, can't I?'

'Yeah!' I replied, not quite believing or trusting his quick change in attitude.

Wayne went to bed no problem that evening and, when he got up next morning, decided to show me the neighbourhood.

'This is where the shops are, we get our videos from here. You got any money?'

I knew that was coming.

'Yeah, I have!'

'Buy us some smokes then, I'm gagging!'

'Did I change colour overnight, hey?'

He laughed. When we returned to the unit, Amy had arrived and watched us from the kitchen window. She smiled and nodded her head as we entered, I knew she approved but it wasn't until I was going off the shift that she spoke to me.

'Work on him, Rob. I don't know yer long but me have instinct you the right feller. That kid need help, them girls too, these people can't control them. You take care, see yer tomorrow.' Amy's words stayed in my mind.

My train was late but I hadn't noticed the time the journey took, my thoughts were running deep. Those kids needed my help – her words played in my mind.

Gad soon joined me and it wasn't long before we had gained complete control of the unit. I knew that control of the children meant that, in their eyes, you were the boss. Nick became a joke, a paperwork man. Nevertheless, someone, somewhere had seen fit to put him in charge of an adolescent unit. Nick Merry was running for the council as a Labour candidate, so his mind was occupied with other matters.

After a twelve month period, I was taken on full-time, which meant that I was a fully-paid employee of Westminster Social Services. The running of the unit was discussed at the main office. It had been noticed that the kids' behaviour had changed for the better and there had been less complaints from neighbours.

'It's Nick Merry who's running it. Well done, Nick!' It made me sick. It wasn't that they gave him all the credit but that he forgot to pass it down. I wasn't really interested in Nick Merry since the kids had become attached to me. Somehow I'd managed to find myself in a 'big brother' role which gave me the advantage of knowing almost everything that went on, even when I wasn't on a shift. In fact, I soon found that it was a mistake having a phone in my flat, even more for giving my number to Nick Merry who would phone me to tell me the kids weren't behaving. I was sure it was supposed to be the other way around.

'Robbie, when you come in in the morning, have strong words with Wayne, Tanya and the new boy Simon, they've been really out of order!'

'Yes, Nick. Okay, Nick. Yes, tomorrow, Nick. Bye, Nick.' For a while, he had me going and I would return and curse the youths for letting the side down.

I even went to Spain twice with the unit. The first time there were four of us, two kids and two staff members, Margaret, Sarah, Wayne and myself. The second time, we took everyone. The little Spanish village was glad to see the back of us that year, too many kids, too long a stay. Familiarity breeds contempt as they say. We'd been there two years on the trot, same village, same hotel.

I'd spent a good three years at the unit and felt it was time to move on. Gad had left a year ago, after clashing with Nick. Gad hated the pretence, as did I, but I'd learnt a long time ago how to play the game. Time had flown by and I'd become so involved. It was late 1989 and Wayne was about to move from the unit. He was now better equipped to face the real world than when we first met and he had turned out to be a nice lad.

I decided to take some time out before joining another agency and seeking another challenge. I'd managed to secure a loan from the bank and bought myself a little, yellow Ford Escort. Having stopped working for Westminster Social Services, I needed something else to do, preferably a job that didn't require solving someone else's problems. I also had a thing about bosses; the people who took all the credit, gave the orders and checked your timing. To me they meant stress.

Gad, with his woman Eva, had moved into a flat on Bedford High Road, Brixton. She was also a Rastafarian and pregnant with my friend's child. By the time she gave birth to his first son, I had become a London private taxi driver. Yes, the yellow Escort was put to work. I'd joined up with a 'no questions asked' firm, running out of Clapham High Street. I was learning my way around the big city with the help of my passengers, avoiding the police because I didn't have the correct private hire insurance. With a large aerial on the roof, I got out of plenty of road blocks. I continued cabbing until January 1990, when my motor gave up. I did take it to a garage, but the cost of repair was too high, so I scrapped it.

I had been surprised by a visit from young Wayne Beckford asking for my help. I hadn't been in contact with Barnes Hall for some time, although I regularly visited Amy the cook, who lived close by. Funnily enough, despite his concern, it wasn't Wayne who was in trouble but his old running mate from the hostel, Nordin Simon.

Nordin was half Moroccan, half Scottish. The Scottish half was from his mother's side and that's who he was now living with.

'His mum was scared stiff, Rob, so was his little brother.'

'Why didn't she call the cops?'

'Cos Nordin sort of brought it on himself.'

Wayne had grown wiser and, although only sixteen, conversed like a grown man. Now out on his own, he was one of those youths who roamed the streets of London, searching for a quick buck or an easy scam. I felt as though all my work had been for nothing, society was breaking down and kids like these weren't being given a chance. Middle-class social workers, who thought they had all the answers, couldn't dish out the discipline, when needed. I had watched the kids being bribed to behave, instead of being reprimanded.

I hadn't done anything about Nordin's problem but the night before Wayne's second visit, I had a nightmare, or was it a warning?

Get the Nigger

I didn't know why I was running but it was for my life. I was being chased along some corridors with yellow walls. Coming to a dead end, I could see through the bars but couldn't pass through. They were coming, shouting and pounding their way towards me.

'Get the fuckin' nigger, get him!' Just as I'd done in my old nightmares about Purdy and Rakim, I shook myself awake. It was just after six in the morning and the flat was quiet, the only sound coming from my alarm clock.

I sparked up the joint that I hadn't finished before falling asleep and tried to relax again. The strange nightmare had troubled me, all those white men chasing me, wanting to kill me.

I was placing an aerial onto the roof of the car because I knew it had to be looked after. It was a firm's vehicle and this was the only way I was going to make a living right now. Suddenly, Wayne crept up on me, taking me by surprise.

'Fuckin' hell, Wayne, don't do that, mate.'

'Did I give you a heart attack, old man? Ha-ha!'

'Listen, I'll run you into the ground any day, never mind old man! Anyway, to what do I owe the pleasure of your company so early? Something wrong?'

I knew Wayne well. I'd become his key worker six months after my arrival at the kids' home and I could see by his face that he was about to present me with a problem.

'It's Nordin. They rushed his house, right in front of his mum, and stole the video and TV.'

Nordin Simon had been a resident at the adolescent unit and had left just before Wayne and myself. He moved out to live with his Scottish mother and young brother, Martin. Mrs. Rosemary Simon had the misfortune of being housed on the eleventh floor of a tower block in Shepherds Bush Green. My first unofficial visit to the Simons' would have shocked me, had I not seen this kind of deprivation before; a single mother struggling with two boys. Nordin, her eldest, at sixteen was the same age as Wayne and Martin was twelve. I noticed immediately the dark bags that had formed around Rose's eyes. She looked like she'd been crying. Nordin was on a high because I had come round to check on him. He had two of his mates with him in the front room, Darren and Curtis. I was to find out that they too were from single parent families.

After hearing again from Rose what had happened, I told her that I would pass by as regularly as possible. She thanked me although I could see that she was close to breaking point. What could I do? Well, for one, I could have words with Nordin. After giving him a good pep talk, which he was used to hearing from me, I told him he could phone me if he needed to. I told him to think about his role as the eldest brother and man of the house and warned him to be careful who he chose to befriend and invite into the house. He had to grow up quickly and I felt sorry for him.

I explained the situation later to Gad. I also told him about my dream, about how it made me think of Martin Allan, back in Liverpool. Why? Perhaps it was because I knew he'd been in a similar place to the one in my dream. I knew Martin had been sent to jail and I'd even visited him there once.

'I think I'm gonna go to prison, Gad!'

'Na, stop that!'

But I couldn't help the way I felt about my dream. Anyway, Gad told me he'd found me a challenge; another adolescent unit, run by a rich woman in Kingswood, Surrey. What made it more interesting was that it was set up to deal with real problem kids; inner city roughs, that other homes couldn't handle. That's why it was out of the city, in the sticks. Fresh country air and rich folk, lots of rich folk. To be honest, they hated the idea of Ms. Hammonds setting up a kids' home in their quiet village. They didn't know what had hit them when the kids arrived. Equally, the kids were shocked to find a private swimming pool and sauna, satellite TV, dishwasher, microwave and more or less anything they wanted from the rich owner.

It only took me a couple of weeks to suss out the show; to suss out why this rich lady should open a private home for these inner city kids. Again, Gad and myself teamed up. We had to, these kids were wild. Having been sent from the boroughs of Islington, Wandsworth and Lambeth, these were the kids that other homes couldn't handle. Unfortunately, their new benefactress and her manager, Mike Farley, didn't have a chance in hell of controlling them either. I realised this on my first shift and these were long shifts, three days on and two days off.

The work became intense, the kids needed a lot of supervision. I also had to turn into a street gangster to deal with them. Again, I began by biding my time, they always tested the new staff but I was soon to find out that these kids needed reminding constantly of who was in charge.

Once more, I was angry to find myself surrounded by textbook, middle-class colleagues with the kids running rings round them. Kids from broken homes, one-parent families, absconders and habitual thieves. Children raised with violence and abuse of all kinds. I'm not saying I had any of the answers for them, or a magic wand to keep them in control. To me, most of it was common sense. I'd been there, I knew the games, who was in charge amongst them. Kids always had a pecking order and it wasn't always the eldest who was in control. Bullies needed to know that you were onto them and willing to bully them on the sly. Once you controlled a bully, you ran the shop, but that required thought, time and effort.

I'd also frequently witnessed and found myself in confrontation with angry and abusive kids. I'd seen staff torn apart by nine year olds. Grown adults left traumatised by tirades of abusive language, even physical attack. I was having none of that. What, spit at me? I've got some of that. Hit me? I'll hit you back. Shout? Wait 'till I shout. Try and scare me – I'll scare you. Talk nicely – I'll talk nicely too. Most kids found it better to be on my good side, not my bad. I again found myself not only being in control but running the show with the role of general whilst only receiving the acknowledgement of second lieutenant. Mike Farley, like Nick Merry, began to use my invisible authority on the kids.

'You wait until Robbie comes in, you wait!'

'Robbie, Daniel has been a bad boy today, haven't you?' Although I'd frown at the child, I wasn't really interested in the manager telling tales. I was supposed to reprimand him, I guess, but so was Farley – he was the general, wasn't he?

I began to get pissed off. Gad had already fallen out with the Kingswood regime. He couldn't hide his contempt for these people. When we learnt how much it cost to place a child in this woman's private home, we both knew why she was in the game.

Gad was a man of principle and he could see as well as I could that it was a farce. Yes, they did have country air, a swimming pool and all the mod cons, but that wasn't solving the kids' problems.

In the course of my work, I saw parents so young I thought they were older sisters. In many cases, that's how their offspring treated them. They had no control over their own children. If their children had no respect for them, how could they learn to respect others? I'd seen the same trend in our youth in the homes I'd worked, from Muswell Hill to Paddington Green and from cabbing in Brixton – disrespect.

With Gad gone, I had the responsibility of keeping the whole place in order. It was hard when I was there alone but hopeless when I wasn't, I was fighting a losing battle and I was beginning to feel deeply depressed. Even the kids had sensed my mood and I knew I couldn't survive on my own, the place needed streetwise people. People who knew what it was to go without, to scrimp and save, fight and curse. Nothing a ghetto child could do or say would shock or intimidate them. For them it would be everyday life.

It had been a warm summer and it was nearing an end. I'd put in for a week's leave. My head was burnt out and my thoughts turned to Liverpool. It had been over four years since I'd left and the carnival was due soon. That same week I decided to hire a motor and go.

Martin Allan

I arrived back in Liverpool in no time, driving a hired Austin Montego. It must have been just after midnight and the carnival was already in progress. I knew where Dione lived and went straight there. My son was three, nearly four.

'You my Daddy, yeah?' I nodded and he smiled.

'Do you want to see my toys?'

'Yeah, okay.' I felt even shier than he did, more awkward. It had been a long time, too long, but, thankfully he looked in good health.

I went out at about two in the morning. I knew there'd be a local blues dance running somewhere so I headed the Montego in the direction of Princes Avenue. The blues music was thumping out loud. The same folk were here as when I'd left, although there were a few new faces. Enquiring as to the whereabouts of Martin Allan and Eddie Edwards, I was informed that Eddie was in prison, Martin at home in bed. I met Ray Cooder, who I hadn't seen for a long time and he suggested that I visit his brother Neil. Arriving at Neil's, the white rum was soon opened and I didn't leave until the next day.

After collecting my son, I began my tour of the old manor. Martin soon came along to join me and I asked if he would like to return to London with me for the Notting Hill

Carnival. He said he'd think about it and then began telling me what he'd been up to while I was away.

'Kidder, the bizzies was on our case. They tried to have me but my solicitor got me out. Eddie, his brief was shit. Anyway, they caught him on camera, selling. I was lucky, kidder!'

So things had changed. Martin and Eddie had been struggling along together, passing in and out of jail. Perhaps that was what my dream had been about, I thought to myself.

'Anyway, if I'm coming to London, I'll have to make some dosh, mate!'

'How?'

'Easy kidder, it's easy. Call for us tomorrow, I'll show you a mission!'

I knew that whatever he had in mind wasn't going to be legal. Neil and the others had already told me about the exploits of my two 'oppos', Martin and Eddie. They had become quite a force to be reckoned with in the manor. I met Marty the next morning and he explained the name of the game. I had to laugh. In a way, it was easy money.

'They can't go to the police can they?'

'No, so who's first?'

'We have to set someone up first, okay. Right, you're a buyer from London. You can chat that Cockney twang, init kidder? Must do by now.' I nodded.

'So you're down to buy weed. When they bring the shit, we take it. That's it, highway robbery!' He was getting excited just talking about it, I had to agree it was a good idea. Well, it was different from social work anyway, I'd had enough of that. I hated the system, I felt like a valve waiting to release.

Setting up the drug dealers was the hardest part. Gaining their confidence wasn't easy. Everyone seemed to be wary of who they dealt with. Anyway, I had hooked some fish and they were primed to sell us two kilos of skunk weed, a home-grown cannabis. The people we were going to rob were home-grown too. They were a Smithdown Road-based firm. Although in the past we'd had people off a lot closer to home, Smithdown was too close but in our madness we couldn't see it. I had to travel alone to fix up the arrangements. Martin had to stay out of the way because his reputation preceded him and, if they saw him, the game would be up. They'd know it was a rip off. That's what Martin had been doing while I was away working in the big city; highway robbery.

'Kidder, they're nervous, they said three o'clock but I think if I had cash to flash it might reassure them!'

'Okay, but don't let them leave with the money.'

'Na, anyway, we ain't got no money.'

'Leave that to me, how long we got?'

'It's just after two now. Is anyone else with us? Might need someone, there's at least four of them!'

'I'll get Masher. It's a pity Eddie's not here, init. He's good at this, our Eddie.'

I was nervous. I was fronting it, if anything went wrong. I also had to convince our prey that I was genuinely buying from them. Martin had given me some wads of notes. Warning me, he said,

'Kidder, that's just for show, don't let them touch it!' I quickly sussed out the reason why. In fact, I had roughly two hundred pounds whereas I should have had two grand. Looking at the rolls of fifties, I realised it was newspaper with a fifty pound note wrapped on the outside. Placing four rolls together, they looked like the genuine article. Martin handed me a miniature Martel bottle to calm my nerves. I had to be on my way soon. Marty knew where the meeting was, he and Masher would be thereabouts, waiting for my signal to move in. The brandy warmed my insides.

'Good luck, mate, and don't fuck up!'

'I won't, I'm an actor, but you be ready, I might need fast out!'

My taxi had arrived. It wasn't a long journey from Granby Street to the bottom of Smithdown Road. By the time I exited the cab, my adrenalin was pumping, I could see that they had already arrived. The crisp BMWs were parked by the curb. Taking a deep breath, I knocked on the large front door.

The Sting

'Okay, okay, I've got the money but I want to see the stuff!'

'Yeah, but my man's not got the stuff here, he has to get it.' 'So, what you're saying is, give him my money, let him leave with it. You okay in the head?'

'Listen, he ain't gonna have you off!'

'Hey, hey, you can't trust no-one these days, mate. I'm staying with me money, that's it.' This was turning into a stalemate. I knew Martin and Masher were outside somewhere, I had to make him move ground.

'Okay, okay, here's the money,' I suggested, withdrawing the bundles from my inside pocket, but as soon as I'd revealed their colour, I pushed them back, deep inside the pocket.

He began to look at me more sympathetically now. He'd seen I had cash and I could tell by his face that I had him, but continued the play:

'Maybe I can come with yer?'

'Na, na, I'll get it now. Give us five minutes. Wait here with the lads!'

'Alright, mate, see yer in a bit then.' I was relieved to have broken the deadlock. The man with the goods had gone to bring them but I had no way of letting Martin know what was happening. I just hoped he wouldn't pounce on the man too early. I had to find an excuse to leave the house before the man returned with the stuff. Although the lads I'd been left with seemed happy enough, I'd have to think of a good excuse to leave.

'Have we got scales, mate?' I asked, praying they'd say no.

'No, haven't you?'

'Shit, will he bring some back with him?'

'I doubt it,' said one of the others.

'I've got some but they're up the road, any of you mobile?' I already knew that one of them owned the other BMW parked out front. Time was running out, the stuff would arrive any second and I had to keep calm. If I showed any sign that something wasn't right, I'd be in trouble.

'Come 'ead, mate, I'll drive yer. We'll have to be quick!' I concealed the smile on my face as I headed towards the front door knowing my mate was out there somewhere.

Just as we reached the doors of the BMW, I caught sight of Martin, his head appeared from an entry down the street. Luckily, the boy I was with was busy getting into the vehicle, because that's when the other BMW returned. He drove right past me to park up. I was already signalling to Martin. He and Masher were moving quickly towards us. In fact, Martin had sussed the game. He somehow sensed the returning BMW contained our prize. He was onto him, the man didn't even have a chance to leave his vehicle. I was already sitting beside the driver and sussed that he was still unaware of what was going on.

'Come on then, mate, let's go!' I suggested. He'd already started the engine. As the car moved, I saw his face change, suddenly realising what was taking place. As he began to brake, he looked across at me, I was manicuring my nails with the sharp-looking blade of the flick-knife I was carrying.

'Drive, what yer waiting for?' Shaking his head, he sucked his teeth in disgust. I made him drive me to Granby Street, right outside the cafe. I knew white boys hated being there, the ghetto boys were too unruly for them. I could see the blood draining from his face.

'Thanks for the lift, mate!' I slammed his door, then only had to wait five minutes before Martin returned. The large smile told me we'd been successful.

'Get some scales, kidder, we'll give Masher his cut and you take yours to the Smoke with yer. You are going back, aren't yer?'

'Yeah, but aren't you coming?'

'Na, things to run round here. You deal with that down there, then come back.'

That was what I did. Returning to London was an anticlimax. I wanted to be back with Martin but I had to deal with getting rid of the skunk weed.

My answering machine was full of messages. Kingswood wanted to know when I was returning to work, I'd called in sick and had been on leave for over two weeks. Gad had called to tell me that Eva was expecting another child. Wayne had also called and so had Nordin Simon.

'Rob, come and check us, mate. Where yer been? I'll phone tomorrow!'

The front door bell rang. It was Adrian, a local lad. I'd been watching my new neighbourhood, observing discreetly who was who. Adrian and his mates hung around the Earlsfield Manor. I needed a driver and someone more familiar with the turf than I was. Adrian, born in London of West Indian parents, was nineteen, unemployed and, like many others, waiting for a hustle. Not that he and his crew weren't up to things already but that was not my concern, not at that time, anyway. I had to get rid of some skunk and with Adrian driving, south to north London were within easy reach. He knew the best short cuts to avoid traffic and heavily-policed areas. Although I only employed him for a couple of days, he told me that if I needed him, he was there.

With most of the stuff sold, I had to travel back to Liverpool. In the meantime, I'd managed to put in a couple of shifts at Kingswood and even visited the Simons in Shepherds Bush. I gave poor Rose twenty pounds knowing I'd feel bad leaving, knowing that there wasn't any food in her cupboards. She complained about her eldest son Nordin and his mates. It appeared that her house had become a place to doss, rather like a youth club. Wayne explained that they had nowhere else to go. Nordin's other mates, Curtis and Delton, were also there and had become a permanent fixture in poor Rose's house.

'Anyway I'm going to rent out the spare room', she told me as I left. 'You know, a student or something, I need a man in here!' Yes, I knew, but right now I didn't see it being me.

Wayne, Nordin and the lads walked down to the car with me. 'Giss a go, Rob, I can drive you know!'

'Not my vehicle, mate. Anyway, you wanna start behaving around yer house, yer ma's having a hard time!' He said he'd try but it was hard for him. The dole wouldn't pay him any money because, despite being sixteen, he was technically still at school. Of course, no school wanted Nordin Simon, and as for his two sidekicks, I never dared ask when they had last attended.

'We have to go out to make money down the West End,' Nordin explained.

'Doing what?'

'Shopliftin' and all that. Anything, init lads?'

'Yeah,' they all nodded in agreement.

'Just don't be getting nicked, hear me?'

'Yeah.'

'And you, Wayne!' Handing him a tenner to take his crew for a MacDonald's across the Green, I jumped into the car. I wanted to say more but what could I say? Stop stealing? Go hungry? Get a job? It was 1991 and there were no jobs. Any jobs that did become available demanded the highest quality. Somehow, I didn't reckon Nordin would last a day on a shop floor.

I drove away from Shepherds Bush towards the White City and felt angry again. Visiting those youths had left a bad taste in my mouth. Westminster had dumped them; no aftercare, no guidance, once they'd left the unit, that was it. They were on their own, trying to survive.

Anyway, I was involved in my own criminal activities. I drove all night, arriving back in Liverpool exhausted. I saw Martin first thing in the morning. He had another mission lined up but I wasn't sure whether I wanted to get involved until I heard the amount we stood to make. Money was the source of life. With money, I could continue to travel between the two cities, even afford to help out Rose, Nordin and Wayne. Dione was also beginning to have a hard time. Money was becoming short all round and I had to think of something more constructive than highway robbery. I had a feeling it could backfire on us in a bad way. Although Martin was game for anything, I didn't want to push my luck.

I still had the hire car and was due back at work in Surrey the next day. I was busy and, in a way, happy that my mind was continually occupied. We'd gone to the Sportsman's pub beside St. John's Precinct. Martin had a bit to drink and was becoming rowdy. I was content to stay sober, I didn't like to go out and get drunk, it was too dangerous. Times were changing. People were changing. Their need to survive was uppermost in their minds. Climbing the ladder, everyone was trying to reach higher, closer to the money tree. Fights broke out over petty things such as 'would-be' plays for power. Who's to be the boss? Who's the hardest? Who's got the best motor? Best woman? Most gold? Those who had all these things had to be strong enough to protect them. It was the 1990's. Those who didn't have, were beginning to take. Kids on London buses were stealing each other's expensive trainers. In Liverpool, wearing too much gold placed you in danger. I wanted to get away from it all.

As I sat beside the bar, listening to Martin telling some woman he was Ronnie Kray's half-brother, an old friend approached. He looked like he was doing well for himself and Martin acknowledged his presence. Danny Smalls was a figure in the manor, having secured ownership of property. He was what the ghetto folk called a 'don'. He could wear his gold; no one stole from Danny Smalls. Danny was related to the Cooder family and I'd met him on the first day I went to Neil Cooder's. We spoke for some time and he told me he had a mission for me, one that he knew I'd be interested in. Handing me his telephone number, he knocked his drink back and vanished into the crowd.

I was left thinking about what it was he wanted me to do. I knew he was a big money man, he'd not long come back from Jamaica. Martin told me he was always out there, hotting in the Caribbean sun. I wished......

'You'd best remember to phone him, kidder, it will be a nice raise, I bet yer!'

Fun in the Sun

I'd experienced flying before on my trips to Spain with the adolescent unit but this journey was much further than Spain. We were on the plane for over seven hours. Although we touched down for refuelling, we didn't leave the aircraft. I was positioned by the window and could see a large sign which said 'Welcome to Florida, USA'. It sure looked hot out there. Not long after we were airborne again, we had to fasten our seatbelts. This time, we had reached our destination.

'Ladies and gentlemen, on behalf of the captain and crew, welcome to sunny Jamaica. We'll shortly be landing at Montego Bay.' There was excitement and chatter around the plane. Most of the people were English tourists. So was I, of course, but I wasn't going to a holiday resort, I was going to be met at Kingston Airport. My only problem was in getting from Montego Bay to Kingston.

I'd heard it was hot back in my parent's country but it still came as a shock. Stepping from the plane was like entering a preheated oven. Before I'd carried my baggage to the customs desk I was drenched. I could feel it slushing round in my shoes, under my arms, down my face. Sweat was pouring from everywhere.

'Hey, man, you want taxi, man? Me have best taxi on de island, man!' He was short, dark and scraggy. I don't know why I got in his car. He reminded me of a pirate, an old sea dog, even down to the squint in his left eye.

'Me hask, is England you's comin' from?' Boy, I was going to have a problem communicating here.

'Yes, England,' I replied. He started talking, but his speech was too fast for me to pick up. I just nodded and made gestures when relevant.

'Me get nice herbs, man.'

'Herbs!' Yeah, now we began to understand each other. He explained, as he pulled over beside a metal shack, that we had a long journey ahead of us. Although the island was small, the roads were in a bad way because they'd just had their rainy season. The island's main bridge was down and as a consequence, everyone on the island had to travel through the mountains.

'Man, roll a spliff before we continue. Unna will need that, seen!'

'Nice one,' I said gratefully.

'A five dollar for that man, you pay later!' I thought there'd be a catch, but five dollars for that bag of lush green ganja was a bargain. It wasn't long before I was hypnotised under the powerful influence of the Jamaican marijuana. The scenery was green and tropical, the soil rich and brown. The breeze from the moving vehicle wasn't strong enough to cool you down nor was it enough to prevent dehydration. I began to get thirsty, the ganja had dried up my saliva.

'A drink, I need a drink, mate.' The old pirate had no problem understanding me. Pulling the scruffy Lada to a halt, he got out of the car and made his way to the boot. He returned with five chilled bottles of Coke.

'Yeah, man, me have everything here, man. Is two dollars each, seen!' I had the feeling that by the time we reached Kingston, the old black pirate, going by the name of Jeremiah, would have made a month's salary.

There were folks standing on the roadside surrounded by baskets and tables of fruit and hot food. I had never seen so many vibrant colours, from the clear blue of the sea water, to the towering mountains and green hills. Palm trees seemed to line the roads, mapping the route from one side of the island to the other. Women glided by, carrying large baskets on their heads. Kids as young as five, stood bartering their wares to passing tourists.

'Cool and fresh, catch a fresh. See it here, cool and fresh!' The cab had slowed down for traffic. A small face had taken the opportunity to approach the open window.

'You want a fresh, English, you want a fresh? One dollar, hold a fresh!' I wondered how he knew I was English. Before I could ask, the old pirate was cursing.

'Hey, my customer, dis man, move from me car. Move, me have fresh for me customers!' The young boy didn't argue but answered the old sea dog with a loud sucking noise from his small teeth.

As we continued our journey, I started to think about the

mission I'd been sent to accomplish. I was supposed to meet Danny Smalls in a place called Linstead. I was told it was a town, just outside Kingston. I was a bit nervous about the mission but I'd accepted it now and had already been paid. Danny had fronted five grand, I knew he'd be really vexed if I turkeyed out at the last minute.

However, I had a week to enjoy myself first. That's if I could, I had something riding on this mission. The day Danny explained what he wanted me to do, I saw the opportunities for myself. He told me that he could have chosen somebody else but needed someone with an address outside Liverpool. The fact that I was working was a bonus, I had a fifty-fifty chance of success. He'd given me five thousand pounds to set things up. I shopped around and saved on two. Two weeks before he flew out here, I had given him a thousand pounds back. Provided I had the money to purchase my own parcel, he agreed that I could. As for his own parcel, I had to be sure that his stood the best chance of getting through. He had financed the mission, I had found and groomed his courier. As I couldn't afford my own courier, I would have to take the chance myself. For some reason, I already had a bad feeling about it. I was sure something was going to backfire on me.

The Mission

The heat from the hot, Caribbean sun stopped me from moving about during the day. Danny Smalls seemed to have acclimatised to the heat and moved about like a native of the island.

Maybe it was because I was on such a mission that the week flew by so quickly. It was the evening prior to our departure and the stuff had arrived. Tightly wrapped inside large bread buns were nine kilos of pure, Jamaican sensie. I was right, there was much too much for one person to carry. My courier was already booked to carry Danny Small's four and a half kilos, I would have to take the chance now and carry my own. My last night on the island passed too quickly. The long drive from Kingston back to Montego Bay was made in silence.

I'd already calculated how much I stood to make from my share, twenty-four grand – that's if I got through the green channel at Gatwick Airport. My suitcase was solid, the bread buns packed securely and covered with clothing.

Having arrived at Montego Bay Airport, we allowed the courier to check in first. I was taken to a house where I had to wait until the last minute, before checking myself in for the return flight. This was the easy part. I had been told that Jamaican customs weren't that scrupulous at searching bags properly. I'd caught sight of my courier boarding the plane. We had to keep separate, if one was caught, the other would pass through. I began to pray for success.

'Ladies and gentlemen, fasten your seat belts!' My heart was racing now. We'd arrived back in England. The sky was grey and the rain storming down. As soon as I entered the airport, I rushed to the front of the queue. Customs had to check you back into the country.

'Did you have a pleasant holiday, sir?' The female officer enquired.

'Yes, thank you.' I smiled, as she handed back my passport.

That was one hurdle out of the way, now I had to reach the luggage collection point. I hadn't seen the other courier. To be honest, I didn't want to see him, not until we had both reached the other side safely, only then could I relax. A flight from Amsterdam had just arrived too. I realised this would add to the confusion. As I waited for my suitcase to appear on the conveyer belt, I began to sweat as if still in the heat of Jamaica. When it finally appeared, my heart skipped a beat.

'A trolley, I need a trolley. Na, forget the trolley just go. Go!' The people from my flight were just coming into the hall. I had my suitcase and was already on the move, the green channel, nothing to declare. The case was heavy but I tried to make out that it was lighter than it was. To my surprise and delight, most of the customs desks were empty, except the one on the end, the last one before freedom. The officer was resealing the suitcase of another black man. I'd skipped past. The tunnel was looming in front of me. Nothing in my way. I'd made it! A few more strides and I was there.

'Excuse me, sir ... sir!' I turned round to look, as did the other folk moving beside me but it was me he was talking to. In his white shirt and black pants, he gestured for me to return to the desk. I guessed at this stage that I still had to play along, although I knew there was no way he'd miss the bread buns. Taking them from the case and holding them in his hands, he smiled at me.

'Do you mind if I put these through our machine? You wait here!' He disappeared around the corner. I felt like running at this point but it would have been fruitless, he'd taken my passport with him, as well as my flight tickets and credentials. He was no longer than five minutes, before returning. He was still smiling.

'You can put those back in the case, sir.'

'Back in,' I thought, 'he can't have seen what was inside.' I quickly zipped up the case.

'Would you like to come with me? This way, bring the case with you.' This was said like a request but it was plainly a command. The passengers from my flight were entering the channel. I didn't see my courier until I was escorted towards a set of doors, I just prayed he'd make it.

They were very thorough in their work. Revealing what was inside the bread buns, they requested I had a photo taken with the stuff I'd tried to import.

'It smells like good stuff, Robert,' commented the arresting officer, clearly proud of his success, telling me it was his fifth one that week. That's when he asked about the tickets. I'd paid in cash for two tickets. He now wanted to know who the other person was. The name clearly said Mr. N. Simons. I knew I couldn't reveal who the youth was.

'Go and see if anyone's waiting for Robert outside,' he suggested to his colleague. I smiled at him, whilst desperately praying that Nordin had gone.

'I reckon this Simons feller organised this, you're just a courier. Is that it, Robert?' I smiled again, knowing this made him think he had sussed the play.

Well, I had been nicked fair and square and was quickly taken to Horsham Police Station and formally booked. They assured me that I'd get bail from court in the morning but for the first time in my life, I found myself spending the night inside a cold police cell.

From fun in the sun to a cold concrete cell in Horsham, England. I was totally gutted and soon began to realise what I stood to lose. They'd found the Kingswood address, that was where I'd booked the flight tickets from; the adolescent unit in Surrey. Customs had steamed the place, expecting to find a den of criminal activity and imported drugs. I began to realise that I was now unemployable. I kicked the cell wall, as I had done numerous times since the door had slammed shut. I knew the mission was doomed, I just hoped that Nordin was okay. If he'd been caught, then I knew I'd be in deep shit.

It was a long night. In fact, the longest night I'd had in two months. I knew what was ahead of me now. I'd never get another job working with kids. In many ways, I didn't want one, I was sick of the hypocrites; the ones who only pretended to care. To them it was a job, to me it meant more. I was angry at the way the youths had been dumped, at how a rich person could be allowed to make even more money from the misery of the young, advertising her establishment as a home for special needs children when she didn't have the staff, or the equipment, to deal with their needs. It was all a scam, a money-making venture. But was I any better than her, having done what I'd done? I looked around the cell as the cold light of day began to appear. I felt tired, smelly and cold.

I began to think of Martin Allan and Eddie Edwards, they had both been through this. Now I knew what it was like, or so I thought.

A Criminal Record

Horsham Magistrates granted me bail. I was happy to see my friend Neil Cooder and his brother sitting in the public gallery. I was even happier to see Nordin Simon and young Wayne with them. He'd made it. Nordin had made his own way from the airport and phoned Neil. There was a large bottle of white rum waiting in the car. I just wanted to smoke a large spliff and relax. I had a lot on my mind now. Things were going to have to change, my lifestyle for one. I was now a criminal.

After a short stop at Shepherds Bush, we headed for the motorway. Nordin was on a natural high; he was going to be paid for his success as soon as Danny Smalls arrived back. We would have to wait two days, then I was also going to receive a kilo and a half of Small's stuff. That was part of the deal if things went wrong. It was a long way from twenty-four grand but I reckoned if I worked, the money would be okay. For two whole days and nights we waited for Small's return. Nordin was to return to his family in London. I wanted to start work, I had to turn my little share into cash and quickly.

I began to feel like the old sea pirate. By the time we returned to London, I had hired myself another vehicle. Adrian was recalled to drive and assist me in selling my wares from Brixton to Wandsworth and back to Liverpool. I had been activated, money was my goal. It wasn't long before the money raised from the cannabis was re-invested, this time into Ecstasy tablets. It was mid-summer 1991. E's were the latest designer rave drug, selling at between twenty to twenty-five pounds each.

Employing Nordin and his friends from Shepherds Bush took its natural course. It became an alternative to shoplifting and recklessly mugging people around the area. Going to acid raves and making money was safer for them. They were now my lads and, before long, street kids from all over the manor were becoming involved. Cheque books, credit cards, stolen jewellery, watches and gold all came flooding in. Getting myself a mobile phone became a necessity and it wasn't long before I moved into the 'kiting' game, employing people to go shopping with stolen plastic. As the youths of Shepherds Bush acquired them, my firm in Wandsworth went shopping with them. I was soon wearing the latest designer clothes and footwear, earning more money than I'd ever done before.

The fact that everyone around me was happy, meant to me that I was doing the right thing. I didn't see any other option now, I was probably going to jail anyway. My second court appearance was due in a couple of days. Before that day arrived however, something more sinister happened. It was 10th September 1991. With a mountain of designer clothes, I decided to make a journey to Liverpool. I asked Adrian to drive me, as I'd been on the go all week. We could do a round trip, drop off the clothes, get paid and make our way back to the big city. The fact that the boot of the vehicle was full of stolen clothes didn't seem to bother us. If the police stopped us, we'd have a hard job explaining it. We didn't anticipate being stopped, and, as it was, the journey was uneventful. We returned to Earlsfield at about ten thirty on Thursday evening.

Having visited my flat and had a drink, I dropped Adrian at his house and promised to collect him in the morning. The engine was hot and the mileage clock had doubled from what it was. I decided to visit the Simons'. Nordin, Wayne and his fast-growing firm had money to give me. Just after eleven I crossed Hammersmith Bridge and passing a garage on my way, I bought extra cigarettes knowing that Rose would be out of them by now. Living on the eleventh floor with two teenage sons and all their mates wasn't an easy task. I buzzed the intercom to gain entrance. It was quite a while before the voice asked who I was.

'It's me, Rob.' The door release sounded with a click. I was in and heading for the lift. I didn't think anything of the fact that Nordin and two of his mates were standing in the hallway.

'Alright, mate?' enquired Nordin.

'Yeah!' I replied, moving into the living room. That's when I noticed the young girl standing behind the door. I said 'hello' and continued into the room. It wasn't until I'd emptied my pockets that I heard the scuffles by the front door. I stepped out to see what was going on. The young girl I'd seen before was being dragged from outside the door, back into the flat. They were beginning to make a lot of noise. Looking towards Nordin's mother's bedroom, I could see the glow from her television set. Rose would be fed up with this, I thought to myself.

'Hey, stop that, what are you lot doing?'

'Ah, she's just a slag!' came their reply, but I wasn't having that. She had been dragged along the hallway floor and looked under stress.

'Are you okay?' I asked her, genuinely concerned. I was tired and didn't need any of this, I had planned to rest here for a while. She nodded, confirming she was reasonably okay, but I still wasn't convinced.

'Here, come in here,' I suggested to her. As she entered the room, I closed the door on her and confronted Nordin.

'What's happening here, mate?' I asked.

'Ah, nothin', she's just a mate!' I knew I wasn't going to get any sense out of him. Wayne wasn't here, he wouldn't lie to me but Nordin would. I decided to go in and ask her myself. Closing the door on the lads, I lit myself a cigarette.

'Are you alright?'

'Yes, I am now you're here, thanks.'

'Was they getting a bit rough, was they?'

'Yeah, can I have a cigarette, please?'

'Yeah, sure. Tell me, what were you doing here?'

'Ha, they told me there was a party.'

'Did they?' After giving her a light and a drink of my Lucozade, I asked her if she wanted me to take her home.

'I told me dad I was staying at a friend's house.'

'Where's that?'

'Chessington.'

'Come on then, I'll take yer there.'

'Na, I can't, erm … can't I stay here with you?' My instincts should have told me to say no but I didn't. Having asked her how old she was, I was satisfied she wasn't a minor. She said she was nearly seventeen, not that I'd thought of anything happening between us. Nordin came to the door.

'Hey Rob, can't we come in?'

'No! Send them home first!' His mates shouldn't have been here this late anyway. I was tired and began to doze on the sofa. She came over and sat beside me. I noticed how much older she looked close up. How she happened to give me oral sex was something that just seemed to occur but we were interrupted by the entrance of Nordin.

'See, you just wanted her for yourself!'

'Get out, fucking get out!' His intrusion upset me and also brought me to my senses. I was wet and felt dirty.

'I won't be long,' I informed the girl. I'd remembered my kitbag containin my towel, toothbrush and change of clothes but I'd left it in the car. Nordin and his two mates, Curtis and Delton, had fetched the portable from his bedroom. His young brother was asleep, so they set it up in the hallway.

'Hey, leave her alone, I'll be back in a minute!' I told them on my way out. I couldn't have been gone for more than ten minutes. On my return, Curtis came stumbling from the front room, his pants around his ankles. In panic, I quickly entered the room but found that she was okay, she'd seen her way to lighting up another cigarette. I'd already had to share a joint with her. I couldn't see myself getting any rest here, not with all this going on. That's when I changed my mind.

'Nordin, get all these people out of yer house! You heard. Come on, girl, you'll have to go and you two. Go home!' They did as I told them. Nordin went to bed and I crashed out on the sofa. It wasn't until mid-afternoon, that his mother woke me and thanked me for sending the others home. She had been awake but I wasn't surprised that she didn't tell them to leave herself, she'd lost control of the situation.

By four o'clock, I was travelling up the M6 towards Liverpool on business. Between the two cities, I was making my money. I even felt carefree, a bit too carefree for my own good. Although I was aware of my court date looming, I was still happy. The thought of going to prison didn't bother me. I'd been told I'd get eighteen months at the most. I wasn't expecting things to take the nasty turn they took, plunging me into the pits of hell.

The Pits of Hell

I'd had a profitable week. I needed one. It was September 27 and I had to travel from Liverpool directly to Horsham. I was about to plead not guilty to knowingly importing cannabis resin. It was just after eleven am when I arrived in London. I wasn't due in court until two that afternoon. Adrian wasn't around, so I allowed another lad to drive the car. Jeff was part of the Wandsworth firm.

'Need to go Shepherds Bush, Jeff.'

'What, by Nordin's and that?'

'Yeah, by Nordin's and that.' I expected Nordin to still be in bed and Rose to be already up and about. I was right about one thing, Rose was up and had left the flat but so had Nordin and everyone else. The flat door was wide open on my arrival and it worried me. Where were the Simons? What had happened? The flat looked a mess. Something told me to leave the place and quickly. Eventually, getting back to the car, I mentioned my concerns to Jeff.

'The front door's wide open, what's happened?' Just as I spoke, Wayne appeared. His face showed deep concern, the information bursting to get out.

'Rob, trouble Rob, big trouble. Them lot have all been arrested.'

'What for?'

'Rape! They've been accused of rape and the coppers are looking for you!' The silence that prevailed seemed to last for ages.

'Y-you sure, Wayne?'

'Yes, Rob, honest, mate! What you gonna do?'

'I dunno. Shit! Shit! Rape! You sure?' I knew he was. Wayne enjoyed a joke but I knew him well enough to know he wasn't joking now. I told him to wait at the Simons', Rose had to return soon, hopefully before one o'clock. That would leave me an hour to reach Horsham. I needed to know what was going on before I turned myself in. Jeff realised the urgency and had me in Brixton in no time. I had to see Trevor, seek his advice. They had arrested the youths for rape and were after me too. I hadn't a clue what was happening, my world was caving in.

'Gad, honest mate, I don't know what's going on, I'm scared, mate!' Gad's woman, Eva, had overheard my distress. I didn't want to go anywhere near Horsham Magistrates. It had gone one o'clock already and it would take forty minutes to get there, Jeff would have to drive. My head was in so much confusion. I should hit the M1 back to Toxteth. But rape – I hadn't raped anyone. Time was running out. I had to make a decision.

'Listen Rob, if you didn't do it, then go. You know you have nothing to hide. Run now and you'll have to keep running. But it's your play!' I knew my old friend was right, I had nothing to hide. Having cleaned myself up, I finally departed. It was fast approaching one forty-five and I was going to be late. The journey to Horsham, where my appearance on importing was well underway, was made in tense silence. I don't think Jeff knew what to say, I certainly didn't. The closer we got to the little town, the more I wanted to tell him to turn around.

'Jeff!'

'What, mate?'

'What would you do?'

'I don't know, honest!'

'Shit!'

The sign looming up said 'Welcome to Horsham'.

'Jeff, if I don't come back out, take care of the runnings with Adrian. Sell the clothes and get the car back to Liverpool. It's not hired out in my name it's me spars. He'll screw, so get it back!'

We parked outside the grey court building and I had my last smoke. Jeff locked the car and came with me. The little court's waiting area was empty. Someone was sitting at the enquiries desk as I slowly approached.

'Hello sir, can I help you?' It was an oldish lady wearing glasses.

'Yes, I was due to attend court here earlier this afternoon. But I've travelled from Liverpool and got delayed in the traffic!'

'I see, what's your name, please?' She already had the phone to her ear.

'Er, Suilerman, Robert Suilerman.'

'Just take a seat, Mr. Suilerman.' I didn't get the chance, they were already approaching from the front door. Jeff looked at me, as the two uniforms walked towards us.

'Suilerman, Robert?'

'Yep, me!'

'Come on, Robert, there was a warrant served for you, you didn't attend, we'll have to take you down, you can explain why you were late to the magistrate. They've been waiting but I think your brief's gone!' This was said as they escorted me through the doors, with huge keys locking them behind me. Eventually, reaching the front desk, the chubby sergeant spoke,

'Ah, Mr. Suilerman, everyone's been looking for you. Nice of you to turn up. So you'll go up in front of the magistrate. Take him up, lads!'

I was getting confused now, no-one had mentioned rape, not yet, anyway. The small courtroom was so empty. My solicitor had left an understudy who approached me as I stood in the dock.

'Listen, you're pleading not guilty, right? Okay, a trial date will be set. There's also another matter, have they told you?'

'No!'

'Okay, let's get this out of the way!' I caught sight of the Customs officers. He began to shake his head in my direction – the one who'd found the bread buns. We all stood as the magistrate entered. I pleaded not guilty. The prosecution didn't object to giving me bail, as I did turn up with a valid excuse.

'But we are led to believe,' this is the part I clearly remember, 'we are led to believe, that members of the Metropolitan Police wish to interview Mr. Suilerman, in connection with another very serious matter!' I looked at Jeff, shaking my head. He knew the script. I was taken back to the cells. The Met boys were on their way back, they'd been waiting all day. The chubby, village-style sergeant, told me it was something to do with rape. I already knew this and phoned my solicitor. She couldn't be at Hammersmith Police Station but would send a colleague and I was to listen to everything he said.

'And don't be intimidated by them, be careful, okay? They're not known for their tact. Just stay cool until my colleague arrives.' I was returned to the cell and sat on the edge of the concrete slab. I assumed people were supposed to sleep on them and shuddered at the thought. That's when I heard them, they'd come for me – London's finest – the Metropolitan Serious Crime Squad.

'Alright lads, how are you? So you've got him for us?'

'Yes, you'll have to sign for him, though, and I think Customs want a word.' I already knew about the good cop, bad cop routine, so I was ready for them. The keys at the gate told me it was my time. In fact, I was the only prisoner in the little station's cells.

'Come on, son!' It was the chubby desk sergeant. There were three of them and they all wore grey suits, white shirts and red ties. As the sergeant ushered me towards them, I noted they were all of the same height, almost replicas of each other, except for their hair and eye colour.

'Robert Suilerman, my name's Detective Sergeant Johnson, these are my colleagues. You know why we're here, we're going to take you back to Hammersmith, where we'll conduct an interview with you. You have contacted a solicitor, we believe?'

'Yes'

'Good, then let's get some handcuffs on you and be on our way!' I'd not been put in handcuffs before and I really felt like a criminal now. It wasn't until we had left the town of Horsham that they started to talk. I'd been placed in the back seat, sandwiched between two grey suits.

'Well, I'm glad you turned up after all. I didn't fancy going to – what's that place, Dave? Toxteth, that's it. I didn't fancy that at all, Robert.'

'He's not saying much, is he Sarge? Don't you like us, Robert?'

'What about football, Robert? Liverpool are my favourite team!' The fields, trees and roadside glided past as I continued to gaze out of the front windscreen.

'Okay, Robert, let's talk about what happened. Do you know a young girl by the name of Juliet Mortimer?'

'No.'

'Well, let me tell you about Juliet and how she reckons she knows you. You do know Nordin Simons and his two mates, Delton Wright and Jordan Brown, don't you?'

'Yes.'

'You see, we know what took place that night Robert. That girl was continuously raped, not by you, we know this, she even says you came to her aid. Okay, now Robert, what we want to know from you is all the things those other dirty bastards did and we know you can tell us!'

'They need putting away for a long time, Robert!' came the other voice.

We'd entered the city, the pleasant scenery suddenly blocked out by concrete buildings and exhaust fumes. I could hear what they were saying but I'd been told to say nothing to them and, even if I did, I was in the dark about any rape.

Wormwood Scrubs

My legal representative arrived twenty minutes later as the interview was due to commence. I was surprised to see that it was a black geezer that my solicitor had sent. He seemed on the ball and told me not to say anything in the interview, not even yes or no.

'This is a serious case, we don't want these stitching you. They're bad boys here, Hammersmith Police had a man dead in the cells last week. We've got the case as well. Anyway, say nothing, okay?' London's finest had entered the room. They were primed and I was their target. The interview began with them asking me what I did for a living. I told them I was unemployed, as I was, at that time.

'Yes, we know this but what did you used to do? Social work, that right Robert? For the benefit of the tape, Robert didn't reply. I'll continue. Is that not how you came into contact with Nordin Simons? You were his social worker, weren't you, Robert? Are you going to answer any of our questions, Robert?' I really began to feel under pressure now. I looked at my legal, he shook his head but I kept thinking about what Trevor had said, 'You didn't do it, you've got nothing to hide.' I looked again at my legal. He frowned.

The copper continued, 'Robert, you do know Jordan Brown, don't you?' Well, I'll tell you, he shit himself when we had him. He says he knows you, says you were there that night. What do you say, Robert? Okay, for the record, Suilerman makes no reply ... interview terminated!' I breathed a temporary sigh of relief, until he spoke again.

'Okay, let's book him. Would you and your client come to the desk?'

Shit! What was happening here? The desk sergeant asked what the charge was.

'This one,' replied Johnson, 'rape and indecent assault!' My face collapsed visibly. The silence at the desk was ominous as the sergeant wrote out the charge – rape and indecent assault.

Why? Why? Why? I screamed the question at him from inside my mind. He was smiling at me now. The water began to well in my eyes but I couldn't allow him to see he had me.

'Okay, slam this one away!' commanded the sergeant. The keys advanced.

'We'll see you in court in the morning. Don't worry, they've got nothing, okay?' My legal was on his way home, I wasn't. 'Don't worry,' he'd said. My mind was in bits when D.S. Johnson returned to take my prints.

'Tut, tut, that legal of yours was no good, he's left you in the shit. Your fault!'

'But-but!' I was talking now. I had to talk now.

'You want to make a statement now? Okay, okay let's do the prints first and we'll see if we can swing bail in the morning!' The new interview began. This time I had no legal present.

'Robert, do you know Nordin Simons?'

'Yes.'

'Did you meet him through your work as a social worker?'

'Yes.' Everything was just sweet, until we reached the subject of Juliet Mortimer and rape.

'Okay, Robert, so you didn't get there until twelve. She'd been there since ten. Those boys continually raped her, then you came in and joined in?'

'No, I didn't see no rape.'

'But you saw the young girl?'

'Yes.'

'She was under stress, wasn't she?'

'No, not really.'

'You took advantage and made her give you a blow job, didn't you?'

'No, she did that of her own free will.'

'Oh, that's not what we heard!'

'Okay, then, I asked her if I could take her home. She said she can't go.' I went on to tell them my story, how I offered to drive her to Chessington, not that I knew where that was. I could see he wasn't happy, I wasn't giving him what he wanted. He wanted the youths on a plate – wanted me to say that they'd raped her. The fact was, I wasn't there when such things had supposedly taken place. Having explained this, I think I pissed him off. I felt I'd wasted my time trying to be honest. He returned me to the cell and I began to cry silently. What was happening to me? I'd been accused of rape. I'd never felt more alone in my life.

I think I almost slept. Sudden noises kept waking me: doors slamming, keys jangling. Daylight appeared quickly. The noise of more keys. Breakfast. Eggs on toast, a cup of tea. I felt dirty. The clothes I'd been wearing began to smell.

'Suilerman, come on, let's be having you!' That meant it was time for my appearance at Marlborough Road Magistrates Court. I went in what they called the 'sweat box', although I could have walked, it was only around the corner. Helen Moorfield, my solicitor came in to see me. She'd met me on a previous occasion but this time I was in a real mess. The importing charge was now the last thing on my mind until she mentioned it.

'Rob, I haven't had the prosecution briefs yet, you know

that will take a couple of weeks. I don't know the case yet other than what you've told me. I'm sorry, but you definitely won't get bail on this, not with an importing charge also outstanding. You've got yourself in a real mess here. Who are the others? Simons, Brown and Wright, they're juveniles aren't they? What have you got involved with?' That's when I felt like crying. She had a way with the dramatics, my eyes began to fill with water. I'd been asking myself the same question; what had I got myself involved in? Oh! God, help me!

I was going to Wormwood Scrubs. They'd told me not to say what my charges were. If the other prisoners asked, I was told to say burglary or something. I was scared now, I remembered my dream, the one when I was being chased. I wanted to scream as I was escorted into the waiting van. There were also other men inside – rowdy men making gestures and seemingly quite happy. Cockneys who were used to the routine, the criminal fraternity. I too was a criminal but, as I was to soon to find out, different from the mainstream prisoners.

CAT A

'Category A prisoner 1149, Suilerman. That's your number. You remember that number.'

I'd been told to strip before having a shower. My photograph had also been taken and one mug shot placed inside a black book. The prison officer who'd brought me from the court seemed to be in charge of me. I seemed to be getting special treatment. Most of the other cons were waiting in a large room whilst I was being rushed through the procedure. I began to feel nauseous and that only made me more anxious. Having gone through all the paper work, I was taken to C Wing on the main population of Wormwood Scrubs. There were cons everywhere, all looking at me as I was escorted to a single cell containing a small bed, a table, chair and also a bucket and bowl.

'In yer go, Suilerman!' As I stepped in, the door slammed closed behind me. I was going, I felt myself going. My head was about to explode when the door flew open.

'Suilerman 1149, come with me!' I began to pant, I could feel myself losing control but held myself in check. I had to follow the officer back down the landing. Most of the cons had now been banged behind their doors.

'Want more photos of you,' the screw informed me. He looked no older than Wayne and the way he spoke to me made me angry. I began to bite my bottom lip as we approached another door which, of course, was locked. He opened it.

'Go in there and wait for me!' It was a store cupboard of some kind, mops, buckets and poles scattered about the floor. The door banged shut, the key clicked in the lock, trapping me inside.

That sound, it was that sound that did it. I began to smash everything in sight. I could hear them coming. The door burst open and I stopped. I was crying, my eyes on fire.

'Okay, lad, calm down now, calm down. Come on, come with me!' It was an older, senior officer with a silver pip on his shoulder. He began to give orders.

'Okay lads, I've seen to it.' They were coming from everywhere – uniforms and size tens. He escorted me back to the cell and again the door slammed shut. I dropped to the mattress and began to cry. Again, the door flew open and a man wearing a dog collar entered, a bible clutched in his hands. Like I'd been possessed by Satan himself, I turned on him.

'You, what the fuck do you want? To feed off me? FUCK OFF! FUCK OFF!' I was begining to foam at the mouth. He scuttled out, the screw locking the door behind him. I was crying out loud now, cursing them, cursing them all. Yet again, the door suddenly opened. This time, a female screw had been sent for. The sound of her voice seemed to calm me and she told me to follow her. There weren't any cons about but plenty of prison officers. Walking to the far end of the wing, she unlocked a door to a different world, the prison hospital. Three men appeared wearing white coats.

'You alright, Miss?' one of them enquired.

'Yes, thank you, Charlie,' she replied. They seemed content enough but still kept their eyes on me. The woman who'd brought me to the hospital said I'd be better off staying the night. I was still locked behind a door but it was a room, not a cell. I was still in a state, my eyes felt swollen and I rolled myself into a ball and began to curse, curse the day my life went wrong, asking myself over and over again the same question, why?

I didn't sleep. The hospital orderlies opened my door for breakfast but I wasn't hungry. Most of the other interns had their food and were behind their doors. I needed a smoke, so I casually walked to the little office and asked for one.

'Sorry, we don't supply tobacco, you don't get paid till tomorrow. Okay, off you go!' I could see the large tobacco pouch on the table and I stayed where I was.

'What did I say to you, Suilerman? Back to your cell – now!' I gritted my teeth and turned away. Another white coat had appeared and decided he needed to escort me back. My hospital cell was at the end of the landing and I stormed off towards it, the white coat close behind. Although I was moving in the direction of the cell, my eyes had focused on the large fire extinguisher on the floor in the corner. The white coat almost seemed to see his fate – but too late. Having lifted the extinguisher to head height, I was about to bring it down on him. To smash it, smash them all.

'S U I L E R M A N!!' The voice screamed my name, halting me in my motion. The white coat who was nearly pulverised, was speechless. I glared at him, before dropping the instrument and storming into the cell. I even slammed the door shut myself before beginning to cry. A few seconds later the door flew open and the white coat came in, placed a handful of tobacco, Rizla and matches on my table and left.

I think I spent a whole week inside the security cell of the hospital wing. They even offered me medication. Seeing the effects it was having on the men around me, I declined their offer. Lycotrel, some kind of liquid cosh. Many of the other patients were shuffling around with no sense of anything. Zombie's, dribbling and moaning. I was glad when I was transferred back to the main prison population. I'd been taken off the black book and placed in a shared cell on the 'Fours' landing, C Wing.

I knew I was innocent of the charges against me and had every right to be with the main prison population but when my new cellmate asked what I was in for, I replied 'burglary!' He was another black guy but right now I didn't know who to trust. We began to get on well, in fact, too well. It was my comradeship with my cell mate that got me into trouble. It was teatime and the Fours had been unlocked to collect their meals. It all happened after we'd collected our silver metal trays filled with so-called food. A confrontation started between my cell mate and a screw. I don't even know what it was over but, because I was standing beside him, I backed him up. My fate was sealed. Within the next twenty-four hours every inmate was informed that they had a nonce on the wing. A sex case, a black one, in for raping a white girl. To make matters worse, her parents owned a public house in Kingston, Surrey. He must have done it. The criminal fraternity's own judge and jury had made up their minds. I was in deep shit.

Under Attack

It wasn't until breakfast time the following morning that I realised the full implications of my position. I had queued for my gruel behind my cell mate. On reaching the servery, I put out my hand to receive my two slices of bread but the little Chinese boy who was serving didn't have any bread for me. I looked at him and he looked straight through me. I grabbed my own and moved along. There were boiled eggs being served by the most enormous black man I'd ever seen. They called him 'Tiny'. I was six two and he towered over me. Still not sure of what was happening, I approached for my boiled egg. Whereas everyone else had been served from the tray of warm eggs, mine appeared from underneath the counter, smashed to a pulp, and was thrown onto my tray. I returned Tiny's intense stare with a frown. The movement of the queue had stopped. All of the other inmates had seen the play. I was on the spot, on my own, and I continued to glare at him. I couldn't believe another black man could treat me like this. Suddenly, a white face appeared beside Tiny's and demanded; 'Move along you, now!'

I wanted to break down but knew I couldn't. I had to stand firm. I turned and began to walk the gauntlet. I had to reach the cell on the Fours. All eyes were on me and I could hear the whispers as I passed. I knew what they were saying, I'd heard the name they called you. It didn't seem to matter that none of us on the wing were convicted prisoners. I knew I wasn't guilty but they had judged me already. I wasn't going to allow them to judge me. Who were they to judge?

I explained my situation to my cell mate. He understood but said he couldn't get involved, warning me to watch my back. I decided it was no longer possible for me to go out on exercise periods, I'd even declined a shower, even though I only got offered them twice a week, if I was lucky.

I'd been out of the hospital wing for two weeks now and I was under maximum stress. I was debating whether or not to squat on the piss bucket, I'd been holding in my bodily function for two days now. My cell mate was out in the exercise yard but something told me to press the cell bell and get unlocked. There were proper toilets situated at the end of each landing. They were foul but better than the brown bucket. I only had to wait a couple of minutes before the door was unlocked.

'Yes, what do you want?' asked the uniform standing in the doorway.

'Toilet, please!'

'Go on, hurry up!'

The landings were empty, most of the cons outside or banged up. I made my way to the toilets. Having found myself some toilet paper, I secured the little door that allowed you no privacy. I was constipated and was straining to clear my bowels when I felt a sudden heat hitting the top of my head. The empty bucket crashed to the floor and I was soaked with hot water. Rushing from the latrine, I ran onto the landing but it was empty, the same two prison officers sitting in the office. They coolly looked at me. I wanted to explode. I wanted to cry. Reaching my cell, I slammed the door, I wanted to kill someone but the cowards had run away and hidden. I heard the keys being turned in the lock. A prison officer burst into my cell.

'Ah, you! I believe you might be having problems here, is that right?'

'No, I'm alright.'

'Are you sure now? We can move you if you're having problems!' He soon left but it wasn't long before the door reopened and another officer came in.

'I'm looking for dirty kit, we don't want any dirty things here, you hiding any, are you?' Quickly scanning me and the small cell, he snarled and and then slammed the door. I began to think about the move I'd been offered and I rang the bell.

'Yes, well, fill this form in requesting a move. Write it to the governor. Any particular reason why?' I just sighed. I knew he knew the reason, he just wanted to hear it from me. I glared at him.

'Okay, I think we know why already. Pack your kit, someone will be over to collect you soon. Oh! you'll be going to B Wing!'

B Wing. It was just another stage in the process of the prison system, I was still in with the main population, just in a different wing. I was padded up with an old Nigerian feller who'd been nicked for importing charlie. I told him my case, I didn't want to tell lies any more. He respected that and even told me about a friend who'd been in the same situation. Although I felt safe for a while, I knew it wouldn't last. Lads from C Wing soon transferred to B Wing and the news began to spread.

'He's a nonce, a sex case!' Again, I began to withdraw. This time, I began to get really pissed off, mainly because it was the white boys, who were on my case. My so-called black brothers had left me to the wolves. Whilst most of them didn't call me names, to get involved with me became taboo. A white boy threatened the old Nigerian because he'd warned me he was making trouble for me. I was on to him.

'Hey, you! You got something to say, have yer? Well, have yer?' No, he had nothing to say, not to my face, anyway. Later, he threatened to do the old man. He was at court the next morning and knew he wasn't returning. I was out for him that morning. Someone was going to die here, they just didn't know they were pushing me too far.

Helen Moorfield, my solicitor, arrived a couple of weeks later. She couldn't believe how much I'd changed, I looked such a mess. I hadn't seen a friendly face for nearly a month and, on seeing her, I broke down. She began to get very concerned about my well-being. Having received the briefs and statements from the prosecution, she said she was angry at what they had done. The girl's statement contained no accusation of rape against me and I too began to get angry. I knew why they'd done it; they knew I'd get a hard time here. I had been set up.

'Robert, she says you forced her to give you oral sex. Indecent assault – that's the charge I see us having to fight. There's no rape on your part.'

'Why have I been charged with it then? Tell me!'

'It's the Hammersmith crew and, to be honest, they're a bad bunch down there. You've heard about the drunk being found with a dead body beside him, well, that's them. So don't you worry. As for your co-defendants Simons, Brown and Wright, they've all been released on unconditional bail But they're juveniles. and, of course, you've got that other charge, that will be heard in Croydon Crown Court before Christmas. You do know that this trial will be held at the Old Bailey, don't you Robert?'

My heart sank – the Old Bailey. Helen went on to explain that they were trying to make a big case out of it – four black males rape teenage white girl. She showed me the newspaper clippings. My whole world crumbled again. It was the local rag but it was enough, I cried again and Helen comforted me until a screw tapped on the window.

'Visit's over now, miss!' She acknowledged what he'd said and, before she departed, she gave me twenty cigarettes.

It was that evening, during the final slop out before bang up, that they finally found the courage to attack me. The screws had turned a blind eye until I was gaining the upper hand. The two lads who'd come to take me out were having problems. I'd been on the ready for weeks. The strength of my anger and frustration was too much for them to contain. As others came to their assistance, I bulldozed my way out of the cell. On the landing, the screws began to re-appear.

'Come now, lads, bang up – bang up!' They continued their routine as if nothing had taken place. I began to go beserk. Passing the landing where most cons had been banged away, it was my turn.

'Come on Suilerman, to your cell, bang up!' as if my welfare really mattered. We were on the Fours landing, there was a safety net, but the drop would break you up. I turned on him.

'You, you – I'll pick you up and dash you over there, GET ME? Now fuck off!'

'What's the matter?' I didn't answer him. The sudden glare was enough and he headed for the stairs, returning with an SO, a uniform with a silver pip on the shoulder.

'Okay, son, calm down now, you've had enough, ain't you? Come down with me, come on!' I followed him down to the main office.

'We're going to put you on protection from now on, you should have been on it before; a cock-up I guess!'

Sex Case

They'd labelled me and sent me to live amongst them; the nonces, sex offenders and perverts, those that had to be segregated from the main prison population, for their own safety.

I found myself in a cell with another black guy, Derek Bond. I didn't ask what he was in for and didn't want to know. I'd already been made aware of what Cat Weasel was in for, two cells away. Cat Weasel was a child killer. Everyone knew he was going to be lifted off. He'd been involved in a paedophile gang operating around London's West End.

It was warm inside the cell. The pipes sending the heat around the jail ran through it. The segregated unit being in the basement didn't help. It was a place where the sun couldn't penetrate. The clammy heat overwhelmed and drained your body of fluids. It was the pits of hell. Most of the men inside deserved to be here. Some of their crimes were horrendous. I began to cry again This is what they had in store for me. They wanted me to live the life of a caged sex case.

December was fast approaching. Christmas and I was due up at Croydon Crown. I still intended to plead not guilty to knowingly importing cannabis resin but my mind was far from being concerned about the outcome of the charge, this was an insignificant case now. They were trying to hang me out to dry, leave me to rot amongst the kind of people who'd offended against me in my past. They'd asked me to finger the lads, tell them what they'd done and save my own skin but how could I lie?

I slept and began to dream of revenge, revenge on all those who had contributed to my present state. Good and evil began to struggle inside me. Cursing out loud, I tossed and turned. I needed help but again, in my time of need, there was no-one. I was alone, like I'd always been. I began to think of my mother, the woman who'd conceived me. I wondered if she knew of my plight, whether she'd help me. But why should she? She didn't really know me. Perhaps I was evil. Perhaps I deserved this. I began to wonder what error I'd made to bring this on myself. What had made the man called God desert me? I screamed into myself, panting and sweating into the musty green blanket. The stench became thick and heavy inside the little cell. My head was in a mess, my finger nails eaten to the skin, my soul searching for help. I'd been alone all my life. I'd never felt more alone than now.

I made a token attempt to look respectable for my trial at Croydon Crown. I pleaded not guilty but it was never going to be easy. The jury listened to my feeble excuses and returned their verdict:

'The foreman of the jury, please stand. Have you reached a

verdict to which you all agree?'

'Yes.'

'How do you find the accused, Robert Paul Suilerman, on the charge before you? Guilty or not guilty of knowingly importing cannabis resin?'

'Guilty!'

'Thank you!'

I was glad when it was all over. The judge, making reference to the case I still had outstanding, began to size me up for sentence. In his wisdom he gave me eighteen month's custody. My solicitor told me I was lucky. Having been caught with four and a half kilos of high-quality resin, I had come off okay. I began to think of what would have happened if Nordin had been caught and not me, or even worse, if Customs had caught both of us on that fateful day. I'd have been in deep trouble but maybe not as bad as I was in now. Who was to blame but myself? My first trip to my parent's country was cursed from the day I agreed to go on the mission for Danny Smalls. Some folk bring back tropical colds, I brought back a handful of trouble.

I was a convicted drug-importer now, so I wasn't taken back to Wormwood Scrubs. This time I entered a different pit – F Wing, Brixton Jail. I had to put on prison clothes, light-blue, striped shirt and jeans. I had 'vulnerable prisoner' stamped on my file and the words 'Rape and Indecent Assault pending trial, Old Bailey, May 1992.'

It was Christmas in a few days and Brixton's F Wing was not the place to be. Most of the wing's occupants were Lycotrel junkies. Men who'd cracked under the stress, freaked out in captivity and been subdued by the mind-bending drug. Zombies – that's what they were, shuffling and groaning up and down the landings. I was offered medication but refused, I wasn't going to become a zombie. The fact that the majority of the men on the drug were large and black had also registered. I wanted to cry for them, you could see that there was no escape for them. I swore I'd not go down the same way.

I received a letter from Gad promising to pay me a visit soon. I also decided to write to my daughter's mother, in Liverpool. I wanted to say sorry; sorry for what I had done to her and her sister. I wanted to say so much. I longed to be far away from the cages and keys, the humiliation of being classed as the lowest of the low, a sex case, a nonce. But I had to wait to clear my name, wait until the real trial, the trial of my life. If I lost, if they convicted me of this hideous crime, I didn't think I would ever be the same person again. I asked myself the same questions over and over again: Was I good or evil? Did I deserve to be here? Was this a lesson, I was supposed to learn? The questions were never-ending.

I was soon moved from F Wing to another segregated unit. At least the cells were clean and contained a sink and toilet and most of them were single cells, so this was a bonus. Christmas passed and 1992 began. I'd got used to being in the little unit and even the fact that we were often called 'dirty nonces' by passing inmates but I still hated them for it. I wasn't a nonce.

I began to read books. Almost like watching films, they helped me to escape my surroundings. Time was flying, it was nearly March. The sky outside the small, barred window was still grey and I could hear inmates shouting to each other from their little windows. It was the same every night. Most of them were on transit to other nicks around the country. I'd been informed that I was going to the Big House. That meant Wandsworth, the flagship of the Prison Officers Association; the training ground for their recruits. Hot-headed uniforms wearing size tens. I was told to be careful in there, just to tow the line. I was still tainted a nonce, a vulnerable prisoner and they had a special wing for us, the rule 43s, sex cases, the scum. That's how all the men on protection wings were labelled by the main population, the scum of the earth and I had been cast amongst them. I prayed for my opportunity to clear my name. Wandsworth Jail contained the biggest wing for rule 43s in the country. In fact, there were three wings H, I and K. I was placed on K.

'You're on the Fours landing 1149 Suilerman, convicted Croydon Crown for importation.'

'Yes boss,' I'd learnt they liked to be called boss.

'Follow that officer, there, and take a kit over there. Oh, and don't ever walk on the centre. Move!' My instincts didn't have to be good to tell me he wasn't so nice, his stern stare and tone of voice was enough. The uniform that I'd been told to follow was younger, he began to swing his keys as we marched towards the iron staircase.

'Where you from then?' I almost showed my surprise at hearing another scouse accent.

'Toxteth, boss!'

'Hey, cut that boss crap, I'm from Lodgy!'

'Yeah?' I began to feel I was getting a break now. 'Lodge Lane, what you doing here?'

'It's a job, init? Anyway, here we are, cell 452. Listen, I'll speak to you soon. What you here for?' I quickly explained my situation before he locked the door. Although the cell was a double, I was on my own for now. It was dirty and I'd have to clean it out and make it decent. Decent enough to eat and sleep in. There were no toilets, it was back to the brown bucket but I was glad I hadn't got a cell mate. Anyway, I'd learned to squat in 'Scrubs,' made shit parcels in Brixton, so back to squatting on the brown bucket meant nothing. Even so, I often wondered why or how men could do this to each other. We were locked up for nearly twenty-two hours a day, with a bucket and a wash bowl. Could things get worse? The uniform who came from Liverpool returned.

'I've checked your file, you're up in May at the Bailey. What do you reckon? Did yer do it?' I just looked at him. He smiled, I shook my head. He promised to look out for me. My first request was to go to the library, I needed my books. For the first two weeks inside Wandsworth, I trod very carefully and observed.

The Verdict

It wasn't long before the friendly uniform sorted me out with a cleaner's job. This meant I was on the servery, dishing out food at meal times, three times a day. I was entitled to extra food, to being out of my cell all day and generally to an easier life. I wasn't really wanting for anything now. I'd got into the tobacco trade. With the wing cleaners receiving the highest pay, I could afford to buy a spliff twice a week. Having not smoked cannabis for so long, I thrived on the small amounts I got. I'd always save it for 'bang up'. When eight o'clock came and everyone was locked up in their cells for the night, I could think, plan my strategy. Having studied and restudied every angle of the case against me, I felt ready. I'd also taken to wearing a blue rosary bead chain with a crucifix on the end.

May came and the sun with it. I didn't see much of it but knew it was there. The jail was hot, tempers high, alarm bells sounding six times a day, the culprits shown no mercy as the uniforms waded in. I began to brew my own liquor, hooch, made from bread, yeast and apples. As the wing cleaner, I had stashes around the wing. We always kept a lookout for security uniforms, they were different from the wing uniforms and were like the inner security of the jail. They'd bring the dogs, searching for drugs, ripping your cell to shreds in search of contraband. Every con hated security uniforms. I didn't want to have any run in with that firm but the way my luck was running, I felt sure I would.

My entrance to the Old Bailey was a cloak and dagger affair. Photographers were out for clear pictures, the case was about to begin. I didn't see my co-accused until I reached the dock. Nordin Simons, the youth I'd taken on the mission now faced the fight of his young life. His two mates Jordan Brown and Delton Wright stood equally accused. I could see by their faces that they weren't ready, to them it was just a joke. They had no-one out there to show them any different, only single mothers who'd lost control. On the second day of our trial, the judge ordered that my three co-defendants be kept behind until the jury had gone home safely.

'I will not have you young men trying to approach members of the jury!' I couldn't believe what I was hearing, that one of them had actually been stupid enough to have done that. I began to get angry, my frustration becoming plain to see. The girl had given her evidence while the jury were watching us, my three young co-accused swinging on their chairs and nudging each other. That evening, on my return to Wandsworth Jail, the uniform I was handcuffed to spoke.

'Wanna smoke, lad?'

'Thanks boss.'

'You know what, son, we listened to that girl and, to be honest, me and me mate think she's lying somewhere. But I'll tell you what, those three mates of yours, they ain't doing your cause any good!' He didn't have to tell me, it was plain to see and I was getting angry with them. They'd all been taken to the cells to wait until the jury had gone. Back in my cell, I cried. This time, I found a Bible and began to pray for help, there was nowhere else to turn.

The next morning the old judge, was angry again. He began the session by having words with my three co-accused. 'It has come to my attention that one of you saw fit to urinate on the walls of our cells downstairs. Which one of you was it?' The jury was scrutinising them. My heart had never felt so heavy inside my body as when Delton Wright put up his hand, just like he was in school.

'You, young man, will not be returning home tonight. Remand him in custody!'

That was the judge's answer to that. I closed my eyes, wishing the three of them would vanish and leave me to fight the case on my own. I began to feel that the pressure was on, the prosecution witnesses had nearly finished when my barrister approached me.

'Robert, don't let the behaviour of those others upset you. We can all see your stress. We may want you to take the stand. Are you ready for that?'

'Yes, I'm ready.'

'Okay, first I have to get that rape charge dismissed, she hasn't accused you at any time of raping her. Okay? We're going to move that motion now.'

The judge directed the members of the jury that afternoon. 'We find that the defendant Suilerman has no case to answer on the charge of rape, I therefore direct this jury to bring in a not guilty verdict.' I began to see a small glimmer of light. They'd dropped the rape charge but that still left me with indecent assault. I intended to fight the accusation all the way. I was going to go into the witness box, in the morning. I was ready for them, I was sure I stood a chance now. If I could prove her to be a liar, then the whole case would collapse. I had to stand for us all, the truth must shine through the lies. I could do it, I convinced myself that I could. I was angry that the lads hadn't got any proper guidance. No-one had taken time to prepare them. All my letters had fallen on deaf ears, all my warnings and rantings, scribbled on prison paper and posted.

To Nordin Simons and the others, this was all a waste of time, they'd been abandoned to face the wolves. Chewing gum in the dock and hailing friends in the public gallery, the street clothes soon replacing the suits, their skin colour and immature attitudes, already sealing their guilt. I'd pulled my chair apart. I wanted to be seen to be separate as I sat head bowed, hands on my lap, occasionally touching my rosary beads, holding the crucifix. I couldn't allow my freedom to be lost this way. Nordin had let me down but he had been let down himself. If I'd been allowed bail, if I'd been outside, they would have been ready, I would have made sure of that. But it was too late now. They weren't ready and the wolves were at our throats. Even now, they still didn't appreciate their plight, it was all still a joke. They'd seen me cry, openly cry at their stupidity, at what was happening. It was a living nightmare.

'What's up Rob? She's messed up, Rob, they won't find us guilty!' If it hadn't been for our uniformed escorts, I would have clouted him, hard enough to knock him back into reality. I asked what had taken place that night, before my arrival. Nordin swore the things she said weren't true, his mum was at home, as well as his kid brother. They had all been advised by their counsels not to take the stand. The way they presented themselves, I could see why.

We were taken into the court room. This was to be my day.

Delton and Jordan didn't want me to go into the box. Their angry objections had filled me with rage. I was the one who had sat in the cells, branded a sex case, spat on and abused, while the three of them thought it was all a joke. I was angry and I had spat it out at them. That was earlier. The old judge entered, I was still angry and I was ready.

'The defence would like to call Robert Suilerman to the stand.' I was twitching to start with; I had to relax a little. My breathing had to be right, the jury were watching and waiting, the old judge peering down over the top of his spectacles at me. It was my own barrister who began. We went through the events leading up to my arrival at Shepherds Bush.

'So, when you arrived at the Simons' at eleven thirty, you pressed the intercom. Did you get an immediate response?'

'Within a second or two.'

'When you eventually arrived in the apartment, what happened? Tell us in your own words.' I explained, as clearly as I could, how I had assisted the young girl who'd got involved in what I considered to be a bit of rough play with the three lads. The fact that she hadn't accused me of having sex with her was the small mercy she showed me. I still hated her for what she was doing to us all.

'The young lady states that you said you'd give her a lift home in your car if she gave you oral sex. Is that true?'

'No, sir!'

'She also says you made a grab for her as you entered the apartment. Is that true?'

'I wouldn't have known whether she was Rose's sister, or a niece. You just don't do them things. No sir, I didn't!'

'Rose, of course, for the benefit of the jury, is the mother of Nordin Simons in whose apartment this alleged crime took place. Robert, could you tell us where you think Mrs. Simons, whom you refer to as Rose, was that evening?'

'She was in the apartment. She doesn't go out much and not that late. She has Raymond, Nordin's brother to get ready for school. It's my belief that Rose was in the flat.'

'Thank you, Robert, I have no more questions!'

Now it was her turn, the chief prosecutor. I'd been watching her since the case began. Straightening her robes for maximum effect and attention, she began to cross-examine me.

'Mr. Suilerman, you are a social worker, are you not?'

'I was, yes.'

'So, when you entered the apartment, nothing told your professional instincts that something had taken place?'

'No.'

'Well, let me explain what happened. Before you arrived, that young lady was repeatedly raped by those three young men and, instead of helping, you joined in. Isn't that right, Mr. Suilerman?'

I'd been told before I entered the box to keep my answers short and, above all, not to lose my temper.

'Whatever you do, Robert, don't get into a slanging match with her,' my solicitor had warned me. But I could feel myself going, she could see I was biting. I wanted to tell them that Rose should be on the stand. She'd been there all evening but I'd been told to keep well away from that subject. Rose couldn't take the stand, she was on tranquillisers prescribed by her doctor. She was unable to give evidence for her own son and all the defence teams had been told she was unstable and to stay clear of her. Nevertheless, she was the only person who could throw doubt on the girl's claims. They'd doped her up and now she was a nervous wreck and the prosecution took full advantage of the situation.

'Those boys had that girl alone in the flat for two hours before you showed up. You, an adult, a social worker – someone who should have known something wasn't right, something odd!'

'I – I would have if there was something. Rose was there, nothing like that could have happened.'

'Did you see Rose Simons. In your statement, you didn't see her until the following afternoon when you woke up?'

'But her telly was on in her room. Raymond was in bed, he had school. I know they were in!'

'We dispute that because the young lady tells us there were only the three boys before you came, Mr. Suilerman.' I hated her, she was twisting my words and lying in order to gain a conviction. But what about us? Didn't we matter? To this woman, it was a job, to convict by hook or by crook.

'So, you received oral sex from the distraught young lady who'd just informed you that she'd been raped. Raped and passed around those three boys. You, Robert Suilerman, wanted your bit, subjecting her to a further ordeal. Isn't that so?'

'If someone came to me. in a motor car, stopped and told me they'd knocked an old lady over, then I'd not be a stable-minded person if I drove the car!' I said it quickly, I don't think anyone understood what I was saying. This worked to my advantage since the old judge leant over.

'I'm sorry but I don't think even I got the gist of that!'

'Sorry, sir. What I'm trying to say is, if you're involved from the start then there's nothing that prevented you. If a female shouts rape, it's an automatic deterrent to any sensible man. I'm not naive enough to climb into the motor. The word rape rings a louder alarm bell and I would have run a mile, to be honest!'

'Hmm, yes, I suppose that clarifies that!' She looked angry, I knew I'd scored points. Clearing her throat again to get everyone's attention, she continued:

'So, when the young lady told you that she had been raped, you suggested giving her a lift home only if she gave you oral sex!'

Guilty or Not Guilty

I had to explain carefully how I knew so much about her, that she lived in Kingston and should have stayed at a friend's in Chessington.

'So, if I know all of that it's because she told me. Therefore, our conversation went further than 'give me a blow job,' but she can't remember telling me these things or asking could she stay!'

'So you would have us believe.'

'You're interested in scoring points, I'm interested in what makes sense, what sounds right, how a conversation flows. In her statement, the conversation doesn't flow right, there are pieces missing!' Of course, I was right. The details I knew about her meant that there was more to our conversation than she'd cared to admit. If it was proven that she had asked to stay after I arrived, then all that she claimed took place before couldn't be true. I was in full flow now, giving it my best shot. She was getting frustrated, I was stronger than she had expected.

'If – if you'd been told your friend Nordin Simons and his sidekicks had raped the young lady; if, as she says, she told you, what would you have done, Mr. Suilerman? Gone to the police, of course, like a good citizen?' This was a trap. I sensed it was a trap. I was supposed to say yes, yes I'd go to the police. But would I? I knew Nordin and Jordan. I couldn't possibly shop them to the law. I was taking too long to answer. Sweat was dripping from beneath my armpits.

'I – I think I'd have told her to go, I think my loyalties would have been split. I would have definitely clouted them, I wouldn't have stayed in the apartment!'

'You would have us believe ... I have no more questions your honour!' My barrister looked happy with my performance; even he wasn't expecting me to argue so many points. After lunch, the defence lawyers and prosecution summed up their cases. The judge would give his summing up in the morning and the jury would go out that afternoon. By the time I returned to Wandsworth, the word was getting around the nick from the uniforms who'd attended the trial.

'He's not one of them, he's been stitched up!' They began to treat me with more respect, like a normal prisoner. The next morning, everyone wished me the best. The taxi firm even sent a stretched limo. Handcuffed to a uniform, we made our way to hear the verdict. The judge summed up and the jury retired as we returned to the cells and waited. My barrister came in to see me and warned that if I was found guilty of indecent assault, the judge would give me seven to eight years, the maximum for that offence.

When the keys turned in the cell door that afternoon, we went on the long walk to Court Two. The verdict was in. I looked at Nordin and Delton. We all held our breath. The courtroom was packed: reporters, the briefs and solicitors, the judge, ushers and jury. The public gallery was also packed but I didn't look up there, I just stood with my head bowed, waiting for it.

'Will the accused please stand!' We all stood, everyone's eyes upon us.

'Foreman of the jury, have you reached a verdict to which you all agree?'

'We have reached verdicts on three of the accused but need more time with the other!'

'How do you find the defendant, Simons, on the first count on the indictment, that of rape. Guilty or not guilty?'

'Guilty!' The waves went round the court room. I held my gaze away from him. As the same guilty verdicts were read out for Jordan and Brown, a cry came from their mothers sitting behind us.

'As the jury will take more time to deliberate the other matter, we'll set a date for sentencing. You can take them down officers!' For me, it was another wait. They hadn't decided whether I was guilty or not. The judge was putting them in a hotel and I would have to wait until the morning. I didn't see the lads again, they'd gone. Whisked away to a life of hell.

The next morning, the jury returned. It was eleven o'clock, the courtroom was empty. This time, I stood in the dock alone, looking at the empty seats beside me, I felt anger for them. As the old judge entered, those who were present stood.

'Members of the jury, have you reached a verdict on which you all agree on the charge set against Robert Suilerman, that of indecent assault?' Again, the answer was no.

'Thank you!' said the judge. 'I am dismissing you members and thank you all for carrying out this task!' Looking at me over his spectacles, he said, 'Mr. Suilerman, we have a hung jury, therefore I dismiss the charge against you. You can go!' I should have jumped for joy but I didn't, something prevented me. Maybe, it was thoughts of the lads, or maybe, something else.

'Hey! You should have a smile on yer kite, you, what's up wiv yer? The judge dismissed it, didn't he?' said the uniform.

'Yes, Guv, but, ah, nothin'!'

'You got to go back to Wandsworth though ain't yer? Yer still serving?'

'Yeah, a few months left!'

'Importing wasn't it?'

'Yeah!'

'Alright, I'll have t'bang yer up until the taxi comes, okay?'

I felt it coming as the cell door closed, I hadn't even got out of the Bailey yet. The door flew open and it was the friendly uniform again.

'Bad news, I fink, yer barrister's down here, he wants to see yer.'

'Congratulations,' I thought, until I saw the stern look on his face. He began to shake his head. The feeling I had ten minutes ago returned.

'We've got problems, Rob, you'd best sit down!'

Angry Man

I sat in the room with my head in my hands, my barrister explaining the situation. 'The judge said and rightly, in my view, that he'd be very disappointed if the prosecution pursued this case, but the police officer concerned was adamant he wanted you re-tried. Even after the judge revealed the figures of the hung jury, and I'll tell you Robert they were nine to three in your favour. If one had been swayed, you'd have been acquitted, anyway, but as it is, the date for a new trial is set for mid-June. I'm sorry!' I couldn't believe my ears. Did they want to re-try me for the lesser charge, for indecent assault?

'I'm not quite sure, Robert, but you've been through hell. I'm going to stick with you on this. It also seems to me that the policeman concerned has something personal against you. That's the feeling I have got!'

My journey back to Wandsworth Gaol should have been a happy one but it was far from over. I hated them, hated the girl and all the people with her. I cursed myself for allowing her to stay that evening and, therefore, having to explain to mummy and daddy where she'd been. How were we to know that her father, a pub-owner from alongside the Thames in South London, hated black people? There we stood, four black males accused of detaining and raping a young, seventeen year old, white girl. I was angry. Three young, black, youths had been found guilty and were due to be sentenced to live a life of misery – she couldn't have picked better targets to accuse. Prime suspects and everyone was sucked in.

I spent the next three weeks studying her statement again, destroying it mentally. This time, I intended to make them look foolish, make them acquit me of the charge. I felt I was being persecuted, they were trying to drive me mad, forcing me to spend time caged as a beast, a pervert, for something I didn't do. I'd begun to get bad-tempered around Wandsworth and that wasn't healthy. Living amongst the sex cases was getting me down.

As the date for the re-trial drew ever closer, my mind was never more on cue, ever more attuned to the one subject – my freedom. My sentence for importing cannabis would be over by November but if they found me guilty in my re-trial, I wouldn't see daylight.

My return to the Old Bailey was greeted by the friendly uniform.

'Ah, you back again? That's right, Suilerman, re-trial, Court Five!'

Seeing her again sent cold streaks of hate down my spine. She stood and repeated her lies. I wanted to pounce from the dock and shake the truth from her but I had a better ploy. The jury looked more evenly balanced this time. The first jury was made up of nine women, one of whom was black, and three men. Any argument by the men stood to be out-weighed, so did any racial issue. That was the first trial, this one was fresh, so was I.

My barrister, a black man, played his part. The fact that the girl chose to add things to my role made her easy prey. Retrieving the manuscript from the first trial proved to be her downfall. My brief proved her to be a first-class liar. Too late, unfortunately, for the three young lads. The fact that she worked in a sauna part-time had never been mentioned before. This time, the prosecutor was a man. He began by asking the judge, if he would make me remove my rosary beads. When asked why, he explained:

'This man is giving the jury members an impression of someone godly. I don't think..!' That's as far as he got.

'Mr. Meadows, let's please have the jury returned. All points of law dealt with and no, Mr. Meadows, what the defendant wears within reason is his business. Thank you and sit down, sir!'

That's when he entered, the upstanding member of London's finest, the copper who had taken to putting me down, D.S. Fellows. He smirked as he passed me. His expression showing plainly that he thought he was getting away with it. To me, his face was the mask of the devil, the one who'd placed the words rape and indecent assault on my charge sheet, the one who knew the truth as well as I did but kicked me in the head for refusing to say things that I didn't see, things I knew nothing about. The smirk sat down behind the prosecutor.

I again entered the witness box. I was surprised by his performance, I had expected a tougher challenge. Although he tried hard, he just wasn't as good as the lady barrister in the previous trial. As his frustration grew, he made comments which were beneath the dignity of a man in his position. The judge stopped me in my stride and asked if I was okay, if I wanted a drink or to sit down. I knew then I'd won. My new jury went out at lunch and returned afterwards with their verdict.

'Foreman of the jury, how do you find the accused, Robert Paul Suilerman, on the charge before you of indecent assault? Guilty or not guilty?'

This time, my fist punched the air, I'd won. The court room was empty, no press, no photographs and no D.S. Fellows, but I didn't care, I'd won.

On my return to Wandsworth, I put in a request to be moved off the protection wing but my request was denied. Although I had to spend my last five months with the sex cases, I didn't mind, it didn't seem to matter any more. The news of the sentences handed out by the old judge reached me; Nordin, Jordan and Delton received eight years each. The joy I felt now turned to sadness before my anger resurfaced.

I was still angry when I left the gates of Wandsworth Jail. I returned to my flat in Earlsfield which was due to be to repossessed soon. I'd been to the Social Security in Tooting High Road who gave me some cash but not enough. Trevor had gone to Africa with his family on holiday. I didn't have time to wait for his return, I wanted to go home. With the arrival of my first full giro, I purchased my train ticket.

'Liverpool, Lime Street, please!' I had time to think on the train. I was now free, but they'd told me I'd never do social work again. Money was already tight. Making it was going to be a problem but I wanted to be around people I knew, where I felt safe.

It was November 29th, two days after my birthday and I was now thirty-one. The train pulled into Lime Street at about five o'clock. I was back. Back home and free. Had I really got away? I never saw them following me but then you never do.

The Further Trials of Robbie Suilerman.

Robbie had had a lucky escape and felt he now had to be careful. He needed to get his head sorted but he was still feeling bitter at what he'd been put through. A man who'd been alone all his life, he now felt the need to be around people he knew. It was nearly Christmas, 1992. Crack cocaine was the money-maker of the day, the streets of Toxteth paved with powder.

'I didn't intend to become a crack dealer but seeing my son and his young mother living in squalor, I felt I had little option or incentive to make money otherwise!' Robert Suilerman.

Teaming up with his old friend, the now notorious Martin Allan, Robbie became involved in the evil drugs trade. Peddling crack became a twenty-four hour business, the money lucrative and turning over fast. Operating Toxteth's red light district, his punters were the local working girls and a few Chinese men from Chinatown. That's how he met Julie Dench. She was an addict and also a prostitute. The day she informed Robbie that she'd just been asked to service two members of London's Metropolitan Police, he was counting money and didn't pay enough attention. By the beginning of 1993, they came for him, for the one that thought he'd got away. The one they now realised had taken the juvenile Simons on a drugs mission to Jamaica. The one who had made a fool of and swayed two juries. D.S. Fellows of London's Met had promised Customs, 'Don't worry about Suilerman, he's ours!'

But Robbie had got away and it was Fellow's job to get him back. Back behind bars. This time, the judge, the barrister and even his own solicitor became tools in a powerful game.

The Further Trials of Robbie Suilerman to be published by the Bluecoat Press.